SANTONI

VIOLENCE

VIOLENCE

JOHN GUNN

PRAEGER PUBLISHERS
New York • Washington

BOOKS THAT MATTER

Published in the United States of America in 1973
by Praeger Publishers, Inc.
111 Fourth Avenue, New York, N.Y. 10003

Library of Congress Catalog Card Number: 73-6200

Printed in the United States of America

To
Celia, Richard and Frances,
bringers of peace
...usually

Contents

CONTENTS

Preface

This book is intended as a short guide to some of the issues and the literature relevant to the scientific study of violence. It is not a new thesis, nor an exhaustive review. Undergraduates and postgraduates studying the behavioural, sociological and medical sciences may find it useful, as indeed may anybody wanting to look at this important topic for themselves.

My profession is psychiatry, a branch of medicine. Inevitably therefore from time to time I come across the problem of the violent person who is sick in one way or another. I hope, however, it is clear from the text that I do not regard violence as largely a product of disease nor do I regard doctors and psychiatrists as specially qualified to discuss the topic. My own reason for writing this book is that a study of one aspect of violence led me into other fields way beyond medicine. Violence like most human behaviour is a truly multi-disciplinary subject.

I would like to thank all those who have encouraged and advised me during the writing of this book. Professor T. C. N. Gibbens first suggested the idea and gave the initial impetus. Many of the ideas were germinated at a most stimulating UNESCO conference I attended in Paris in May 1970, which was chaired by Professor David Hamburg from Stanford. Dr Richard Passingham and Patrick Pope have read the manuscript and provided some most valuable comments. The burden of the typing has been shared by my secretary, Mrs Sybil Halliwell, and by my wife. Miss Helen Marshall and her staff of the Library at the Institute of Psychiatry have been of the greatest possible assistance.

The diagram of the human brain was drawn by my wife from an illustration produced by Roche Products Ltd, and is reproduced by their kind permission.

Without my wife's active support, assistance and, above all, tolerance the book would never have been written at all.

1 *Introduction*

I am a male primate. I belong to the genus *homo sapiens*. One of my special characteristics is that I am capable of and responsible for more violence and destruction than any other type of living creature. I alone am not responsible for all the death and destruction due to violence that I see around me—I need helpmates. Without the rest of you I could only achieve a minimal degree of horror, but together, you and I, plus a few other companions, can and do wreak real havoc. We are destroyers—glorious, revolting, powerful, helpless destroyers. Why?

There can never be a complete answer to a why question; each discovery we make only pushes the question one stage deeper. We are better advised to tackle the how, what, and where questions. If this book achieves anything, it will be in raising more doubts in your mind than you already have there.

'Violence' is an emotive word, and not a particularly satisfactory one—it means several different things at the same time and sparks off different areas of understanding and interest in different people. Could we have chosen a better word—perhaps 'aggression'? Unfortunately all the possible words are unsatisfactory because of their multiple meanings, their rapid change of meaning in the vernacular, and the different emotional responses, or perhaps prejudices, they evoke in different

13

people. It is possible that it is these emotional responses which cause all the difficulties. Do you regard aggression or violence as 'bad'? Always? Even when you indulge in it yourself? Are some wars justifiable and others not? Does the morality of violence depend on who starts it? Would you be as successful as you are without some degree of aggression? If someone is defined as a 'criminal', is violence from him unjustified but to him justified? We shall not attempt to explore these issues in any detail and no definite opinions about them will be expressed. Nevertheless it is worthwhile noting that you and I do have views on these matters, views almost certainly dislocated from scientific knowledge, yet bound to affect our interpretations of that knowledge.

'Aggression' is defined in the *Shorter Oxford English Dictionary* as 'an unprovoked attack' or 'an assault', whereas 'violence' is regarded as 'the exercise of physical force so as to inflict injury on or damage to persons or property'. However, in modern usage a distinction has crept in in addition to the one of provocation. Storr[1] a psychotherapist, points out that we now use 'aggression' in a very wide sense. 'When a word becomes so diffusely applied that it is used both of the competitive striving of a footballer and also of the bloody violence of a murderer, it ought either to be dropped or else more closely defined.' We talk of an aggressive salesman, or of an aggressive approach to problems when we want to indicate success in overcoming difficulties. For Tiger[2] in his study *Men in Groups*, aggression is a social-organisational term referring to a process, while violence describes an event that is only one of the possible outcomes of the aggressive process. In exactly the same way for Daniels and Gilula[3] aggression includes a variety of behaviours, can often be constructive and has helped man to survive. Violence, on the other hand, is damage to another, or attack with intent to damage; it is simply a form of aggression—destructive aggression.

It is because of this complex intermingling of constructive and destructive aspects in the concept of aggression that definition and, hence, discussion becomes so difficult. It is as well then to indicate right at the outset that throughout this book 'aggression' will be taken to mean *an attacking process*, and 'violence' will mean *severe aggression*. Furthermore, all the discussion in the ensuing chapters will be directed to one form of violence—physical violence. Using the concepts in this way aggression will normally be equated with the process by which dominance is gained, and violence usually regarded as a destructive form of aggression.

At times throughout this book it may be difficult to distinguish between intra-specific violence (violence between man and man) and inter-specific violence (hunting). We shall draw deliberate analogies in Chapter 4, but it is usually important to distinguish between carnivorous creatures (such as ourselves) catching their supper (or working in the abbatoir) and aggressive interactions between members of the same species. It is incorrect to cite fox-hunting as an example of human violence in the sense that we shall be generally using —it may be true that the fox-hunters are no longer interested in catching a meal and it may be correct that similar physiological processes are used in fox-hunting as in warfare; but hunting and intra-specific aggression are not the same thing. Some hunters (eg lions) are rarely seen to fight among themselves, and some vegetarians (eg rhesus monkeys) can be violent in the sense we are concerned with in this book.

Another aspect of violence we should keep in our minds is the constructive aspect. 'It is a tragic paradox that the very qualities which have led to man's extraordinary success are also those most likely to destroy him. His ruthless drive to subdue or to destroy every apparent obstacle in his path does not stop short at his own fellows'.[1] Even Darwin[4] himself paid passing reference to the importance of intra-specific fighting in evolution, even though at that point he was only thinking in terms of the stronger male getting the best choice of sexual partners. What are the advantages of aggression, and, more specifically, of violence? Darwin indicated one advantage—

choosing a mate. Extend this notion of choice a little further and we soon run into the concept of power, which gives one first choice in all the desirables of life—mate, food, place to live, comfort, and so forth—enables one to avoid an early death, and allows one to populate the planet with one's own offspring rather than others. Even in this simple way it can be seen how an aggressive animal has an evolutionary advantage over the submissive one, how in fact aggressiveness has been selected in the development of many species. Not surprisingly, if there is intense competition for survival or for power within any species, there is also a special pressure towards aggressiveness as a survival trait. However, aggression carries the propensity to destroy—that is what gives it selection advantage—and the amount of destructiveness can become too great. Perhaps that point has now been reached in human evolution. We have been so successful in triumphing over other species, over other members of our own species, and over our own environment that if we are not now careful we will even triumph over ourselves in a kind of grand suicide.

One point that will be largely eschewed in this monograph is the controversy about instinct. As we shall see in Chapter 4, there is a great debate between the psychoanalysts and some ethologists, such as Lorenz,[5] who believe that aggression is an instinct like hunger and thirst, and other biologists, like Scott[6] who believe that aggression has to be provoked by external stimulation. As authorities such as Hinde[7] have pointed out, this controversy is both false and sterile. The idea that there is a clear-cut dichotomy between innate and learnt behaviour is quite unhelpful. What is required is an understanding of the extent to which nature or nurture are responsible for any behaviour we observe. 'Adult aggressiveness can be affected by the early family and social environment, by early thwarting and achievement by experiences in aggressive encounters. It is more likely in frustrating and crowded conditions. Here is a group of factors which affect aggression and which are within our control. Surely this is the place to start?'

With these authoritative words in our minds, let us begin to examine the problem of violence, and let me at once endorse the view given by Hinde of a group of factors. As we look at different areas of our subject we shall, of course, be looking at the different types of violence already referred to, but we shall also be coming across many different factors related to violence. If one wished to examine a violent event, one would try to tease out all the possible elements—personal, social, psychological, cultural and so forth—and then see them together in a fairly complex interactional system. To draw an analogy, if a car skidded into a lamp-post and we were interested in the antecedent factors, we would examine the road surface, the condition of the tyres, the condition of the brakes, the driver's ability, his health and sobriety at the time of the accident, the speed of the car, the presence of other cars or hazards, the lighting at the time and so on. Rarely would only one of these factors be a sufficient cause of the accident; usually a unique combination would have come together to produce the unfortunate event. It is possible that if any one of the factors had been different the accident would not have occurred—eg a dry road surface instead of a wet one would have allowed a different interactional equation to operate and there would have been a different outcome.

'Ours is a violent age', we are everlastingly told, and sometimes we assume from this that other ages were not violent. Is this a correct assumption? Obviously it depends upon which type of violence you are talking about. We shall see in Chapter 6 evidence that sanctioned group violence is on the increase; but as is illustrated in Chapter 8, in some countries at least, we cannot be so sure about illegal individual violence. Furthermore the trends vary considerably from culture to culture—what is true in India may not be true in Norway, or in China or Nigeria. It must be borne in mind that most of the experiences and evidence referred to in this book will be of Anglo-Saxon origin, ie come from the United Kingdom or the United States.

Time scale is another important aspect. 'Violence up another 10 per cent this year' as a screaming headline must bring a smile to a geologist or an anthropologist. Is it sensible to try and comment upon fluctuations over such a short period of time? In geological terms man is a newcomer to the face of the earth.

Many previous eras and cultures have embodied violence almost as an essential component. Take, for example, the Aztecs. When the Spanish discovered them in the sixteenth century they were sacrificing for religious reasons some 10,000-50,000 human victims each year.[8] Each month, there was some kind of sacrificial ceremony. The ceremony for the fire god included the destruction of a number of prisoners at a dance round a large bonfire, the victims being bound hand and foot, then ceremonially tossed into the fire, only to be hooked out just before they died so that their living hearts could be torn from their bodies. Many religions have embodied human sacrifice, and a study of the Old Testament will indicate that these ideas were at one time part of the Jewish tradition; indeed, the Christian belief that the Son of God was sacrificed for the benefit of mankind is a reminder of this tradition and the Christian Mass is clearly linked to blood sacrifice practices.

Even if we insist upon sticking to the last few centuries of European culture, history would not necessarily support the notion that we live in a particularly violent age. Taft and Ross,[9] for example, in an extensive review of the literature concerning violence among American working people, come to the conclusion that the United States has *had* (my italics) the bloodiest and most violent labour history of any industrial nation in the world, but that its incidence and severity have been sharply reduced in the last quarter of a century. Roberts[10] in a similar review of English working-class history agrees that violence has diminished rather than increased. One of the most vivid historical accounts of this transformation is given by Hibbert[11] in *The Roots of Evil*. He quotes example after example, often from contemporary writings, of hideous daily violence during previous centuries—of torture, of burnings, of highway robbery, of the brutality of armed mercenaries, of widespread drunkenness with associated violence, and of merciless cruelty to children and animals. Of the very recent eighteenth century he writes:

Senseless murders .... were as common as riots. For violence was still an accepted part of everyday life and it was not to be expected in an age which set so little store by human dignity that it could be otherwise. Men accustomed to paying twopence to go and laugh and jeer at lunatics in Bedlam; to watching women knocking each other about with bare fists in the boxing ring; to throwing bricks at defenceless people in the stocks and pillory; to be given a holiday on the day of a hanging so that they could go to the fair at Tyburn and cheer as men and women slowly died at the end of a rope; to seeing their fellow human beings whipped and burned and disembowelled and cut into four pieces; to passing the putrescent bodies of highwaymen suspended in iron cages near the scenes of their crimes—men accustomed to a life in which these things were commonplace were not likely to come to the view that brutality was inexcusable.

References to this chapter appear on p181

2 *Violence in Animals*

For the non-zoologist I should perhaps explain that we now have a fairly clear idea of what type of animal man is, and we have some information about how his present-day structure and behaviour evolved. Man is a mammal, belonging to the group known as primates. The main sub-groups of primates are *Cercopithecidae* (the Old World monkeys), *Ceboidea* (the New World monkeys), *Prosimians* (small nocturnal animals that in some respects resemble the group of mammals that produce the primates), and *Pongidae* (the apes).[12] The apes include the gibbon, orangutan, chimpanzee and gorilla. They have all lost their former quadrupedalism and have elongated arms; the trunk is short, wide and shallow; and the limbs are adapted to feeding in small branches and to swinging between branches—'brachiation'. These locomotive differences divide *Pongidae* from *Cercopithecidae*, and fossils suggest that the families have been distinct since the Oligocene period.

Man, who can be regarded as forming his own separate family—*Hominidae*—is derived from a family (*Hominoidea*) that also produced the *Pongidae*, although only very recently in geological terms (maybe 2 million, maybe 20 million years ago). This means that modern man, who is a newcomer of only 500,000 years standing, is closely related to gorillas, chimpanzees and the like. Recent biochemical studies, for example, suggest that the relationship between the chimpanzee and man is closer than that between a dog and a fox or that between a horse and a donkey. The main differences between man and his close relatives are his upright stance and his total bipedalism, his superior intelligence, his use of tools, his complex communications system involving language, his consequent complex social structure, his psychology, and his diet. The last has a large and very important carnivorous element, very different from the *Pongidae*, who are almost exclusively vegetarians. The earliest bipedal toolmakers (*Australopithecus*) had medium-sized brains and it is probable that some of the distinctively human attributes have developed only in the last 400,000-600,000 years.[12]

Violence is by no means peculiar to humans, nor to primates; many forms of animal life have the capacity to fight among themselves. However, it is probably true to say that man has special skills and attributes for violence, and with nuclear weapons has reached the bizarre position where he is in danger of obliterating himself, indeed his entire species, when attacking a putative enemy.

In spite of this it is very debatable indeed whether man can be regarded as more 'violent' than other mammals. Certainly man has achieved enormous power compared to other species and, of course, he can channel that power into constructive or destructive actions. Whether he actually resorts to violence more frequently than other species, however, is probably impossible to determine, largely because to answer that particular question exactly similar situations would have to be compared and such situations never occur. We live in different groupings, at a different population density, and with different feeding habits from any other primate. Some authorities have looked at the terrible group fights (or wars) that occur among mankind and have said that this indicates we are more violent than other species; but some insects, such as ants, wage war against one another, and even amongst primates other examples of group fighting can be found, as Southwick (p24) discovered when he observed rhesus monkeys. Some suggest that it is because we are the only carnivorous and hunting primates that we are so violent. Read[13] was one of the earliest writers to put forward this idea and as we shall see later our psychology of violence may well have incorporated aspects from our feeding habits; but it is worth remembering that herbivorous creatures can be very aggressive. Baboons, as we shall see, can be particularly violent, but they live very largely on vegetables (grains, seeds, roots) and when they do eat animal matter (ants, caterpillars, mussels, etc) this is gleaned rather than hunted.[14] Surely it is unimportant to know whether or not we are more violent than other species—it is sufficient to know that we are violent and dangerously so. The important questions are related to understanding and controlling our violence.

Ethology

A new but fundamental branch of zoology called ethology has arisen in recent years. Basically it is the observation of animal behaviour in the wild and the classification and description of the elements of the behaviour. Tinbergen, one of the pioneers of this kind of work, has become famous for his studies of herring gulls and for being one of the first people clearly to set out the interactions between individuals who are dependent upon one another socially. Birds are not as relevant for our subject as primates (although Tinbergen himself has made a plea for no generalisations at all from one species to another[15]) and so we will not dwell upon Tinbergen's fascinating results. It should be noted, however, that he clearly describes how a bird will defend its nesting site against intruders, how other birds recognise attack and submission signals, that submission (hands-up) types of signal are almost always obeyed and prevent the furtherance of the winner's attack, and that when birds know one another there is an established hierarchy so that some birds have more power than others, this hierarchy sometimes being referred to as the 'peck-order' and based upon previous aggressive encounters. Tinbergen is also especially impressed by the infrequency of actual bloodshed in situations of the type he noticed and attributes this to the protective aspects of the dominance-hierarchy, since a gesture of submission halts the aggressor's attack. A mechanism he also noted in birds is displacement:[16] a herring gull, when threatening, may, for instance, pull up some grass as if to build a nest instead of pecking his opponent.

This type of ethological technique has been extended to a whole series of different species, including the primates. Carpenter was one of the earliest workers to investigate primate behaviour in the wild, in the 1930s studying both the gibbon[17] and the howler monkey.[18] These two remarkable studies are of special interest here, as they illustrate the spectrum of aggression that the primate world reveals. Carpenter almost never found two adult male gibbons living in a group, the basic social unit being a family of one adult male, one adult female and their offspring. In a colony of captive gibbons he observed that two males caged next to one another showed strong and persisting antagonism, and that they several times bit each other severely through small openings in the wires—once they succeeded in getting at one another properly and one animal ended up with a splintered arm bone. In the wild he did not see much pugnacious activity—largely because the males kept well away from one another. However, even in the wild fights must occur from time to time because captured animals sometimes showed old battle scars. 'There is perhaps some relation between the facts the fights rarely occur and that when they do take place, they may be very severe.'

In contrast to this, Carpenter found little or no evidence of fighting among howler monkeys, which, as their name implies, call to one another with a variety of sounds from a low-pitched sonorous roar to a chirping squeal—many of the sounds having a definite and discernible meaning. The monkeys live in groups of about eighteen, including three or four males. Carpenter's guess is that the low level of overt aggression is explained by a well understood and established system of rules and roles, so that each male responds appropriately to each other male and they do not have to keep testing out the dominance hierarchy. Furthermore, it seems that their postures, gestures, and vocal signals are so well developed that they can act as a substitute for fighting.

Rhesus monkeys have also been studied in some detail. Southwick and his co-workers[19] looked at these monkeys in Northern India in different situations—along the roadsides, along the canals, along the railways and around the stations, in the Hindu temples of Aligath and in the forests of the Himalayan foothills. Considerable differences in behaviour were noted in the different types of habitat: for example, the average group size varied between about ten individuals by the railway and around fifty in the forests. While all areas showed a relatively high degree of aggressive interaction, the temple area showed the most. The number of monkeys living round the artificial lake in the temple area was 104 and they had a mean group size of twenty-six individuals, and a higher proportion (22.3 per cent) of juveniles. Four groups were observed, and there appeared to be a dominance hierarchy between the groups—all groups retreated when they saw members of Group 1 approaching. There were no vocal signals, so if a group failed to see a dominant group approaching it would be taken unawares and then a severe fight would take place. Twenty-four severe inter-group fights and numerous minor ones were observed in eighty-five days of observation. Severe wounds would occur and most adult males bore wound scars around the face, shoulders or rump. Wounded individuals were much less common in rural and forest areas, and Southwick speculates that the crowded conditions of the temple environment compared with the greater escape potential and protective cover of forest conditions resulted in more aggressive activity. Inter-group fights usually lasted only a few minutes, until the subordinate group retreated. Occasionally, however, there could be a prolonged fight of 15-20 minutes duration. The within-group relations of males usually involved a moderately sharp dominance hierarchy and varied from peaceful, even cooperative associations to highly agonistic ones.

One of man's closest relatives, the chimpanzee, has been studied in great detail over a number of years by Jane Van Lawick-Goodall,[20] who has virtually lived among a group in the Gombe Stream Reserve in Tanzania. In essence these apes live in loosely organised groups, adults only associating for a few hours or a few days at a time, and mature males frequently moving about on their own. Aggressive interactions are unusual, but during a severe attack the victim may be pounded with feet and hands, rolled, dragged and (rarely) bitten. Violent attacks, which were only 10 per cent of all attacks and often resulted in no discernible injury apart from the occasional wrenching out of hair, were usually short, seldom lasting more than a few seconds.

Crowding and Social Factors

Southwick and his colleagues[19] postulated that crowding is an important factor in producing fights among rhesus monkeys. They noticed that more fighting occurred in the crowded areas. In experiments conducted later, Southwick[21] showed that a good deal of fighting occurs among rhesus monkeys in captivity, and that one of the several ways to increase this fighting is significantly to reduce the space available to the group.

A vivid demonstration of the violence that can occur in primates was provided by a remarkable series of observations of Monkey Hill at the London Zoo made by the future defence adviser to the British Government, Sir Solly Zuckerman.[22] Almost 100 baboons had been released into an enclosure at Regents Park. Zuckerman noticed a fixed and rigidly enforced hierarchy, in a violent community where brute force ruled the day. Aggressive and dangerous outbursts from high-ranking individuals towards their inferiors were commonplace. Dominant monkeys would grab as much food as possible, more than they needed, in fact, and mothers would even take food from their own offspring—all this in spite of the abundant supply of food provided by the zoo keepers.

Fights were frequent and a number of violent deaths took place. Females, weaklings, and youngsters suffered the most: for example, Zuckerman saw one male attacking a baby monkey, which died later that evening. Out of sixty-one male deaths during the observation period (1929-30) eight died by violence; of thirty-three female deaths, thirty were the result of 'sexual fights'. Baboons, it seemed, were savage violent animals.

This reasonable supposition was held for some time, until observations on baboons in the wild in Africa, where there were no wire fences or other artificial elements, became available. Once again it was noticed that the baboon group was organised around the dominance hierarchy of adult males.[23] Often there was only one adult male but two to nine females with offspring up to the age of 18 months. No observations have been made of one baboon killing another, although low-ranking males are sometimes driven from an established group. Attacks can occur when a dominant animal will charge at another, seize his victim, bite him, and rub him in the dust. Even though these attacks appear very vicious, they are usually short-lived, and only once did Hall and DeVore observe any physical injury to the victim. Furthermore Hall[24] notes that not once did they observe group fighting among baboons in over 2,000 hours of observation, very different results from those obtained by Zuckerman.[22] Just to reinforce the difference Hall in his own article reports a further example of fighting in captivity, this time at Bloemfontein Zoo, when an 'alien' adult male and adult female were introduced into an established group of seventeen baboons.

The resulting disturbance completely destroyed the social structure of the colony and many of the animals were killed or died of their injuries.

What are the possible factors leading to the baboon violence? Certainly not a shortage of food. Overcrowding, or at least, a shortage of escape distance is one on which Russell & Russell place special emphasis in their book.[25] Other possible features are a disturbed male/female ratio (eg, the Zuckerman colony had many more males than is usual under natural conditions), and unfamiliarity. Many of the baboons of Monkey Hill were strangers when placed there, whereas under normal conditions monkeys belong to their group from birth. These social factors are probably of much greater importance than the sheer volume of numbers in producing the devastating violence observed by Zuckerman. The experiment by Southwick referred to above was just one part of a revealing study carried out in Calcutta Zoo.[26] Seventeen rhesus monkeys were kept in a cage of 1,000sq ft, and various measures were tried to alter the level of violence among them. Partitioning the cage into two had no effect as long as an intervening door remained open and the animals could use all 1,000sq ft, but when the door was shut and they were confined to 500sq ft, the amount of aggressive behaviour increased. A much more powerful stimulant of aggressive behaviour, however, was the introduction of new monkeys who were social strangers. In fact, only juveniles could be successfully brought into the colony, and introduced adults (males or females) had to be removed on humanitarian (or rhesusian?) grounds, as they were not eating and in poor physical condition. Monkeys of comparable age and sex to the introduced monkeys were the most threatening to the newcomers. Social changes had a far greater impact on levels of intra-group aggression than did environmental changes.

Nevertheless this is not to say that Southwick had observed no effect just by a reduction of space. He had. Other workers have also noticed this effect in other species. Leyhausen[27] noted that if cats are overcrowded, a despot cat emerges who holds all the others in fear. The animals can seldom relax, they never look at ease and there is continual hissing, growling and fighting; play stops, and locomotion and exercise are reduced to a minimum. Calhoun[28] overcrowded albino rats and found that many destructive characteristics appeared: for example, the normal standards of maternal care dropped so that large numbers of infants (96 per cent in one experiment) died before reaching maturity. Furthermore, both females and infants were attacked (and sometimes eaten) by males. Males tended to opt out of sexual and social interactions, apart from vicious fights, and the occasional male became morbidly pansexual, mounting every female in sight whether she was receptive or not. However, like Southwick, Barnet[29] draws attention to the fact that social factors are more important in precipitating violence among rats than overcrowding *per se*. He demonstrated that fighting is highly probable when an adult male enters a region in which another adult male is already established. Of twenty males added to established colonies, eighteen died, yet there was no corresponding mortality among the residents. It was possible to get stranger males to live in peace but they had to be introduced into a new territory almost simultaneously; even a 10 minute difference could upset the situation.

Sex

In the discussion on animal violence so far the male seems to have been impugned more than the female. This is no accident. There is good evidence that in most mammals the male is more aggressive and hence more violent than the female. Females can be very aggressive at times, it is true, and in some species (eg, the gibbon) there is not much to choose between male and female aggressiveness. The male hamster, in fact, is less aggressive than the female. This does not detract from the general point, however, and there are few mammalian species in which the female initiates attacks more frequently than the male, and is generally dominant to the male.

You do not have to be an ethologist to recognise the general truth of these statements. Among domestic mammals—the dog, the horse, cattle, sheep, the pig, etc—the difference in aggressiveness can easily be seen. Farmers do not keep herds of adult bulls together because of the severe fighting that would occur if they did, but they successfully keep large herds of cows.

Equally one does not need to be physiological zoologist to guess that this sexual difference in aggressiveness is related, fairly directly in mammals, to the sexual hormones. For hundreds of years, without understanding the physiology of the process, man has castrated some male animals to make them more amenable. The ox is a castrated bull. In a review of the relevant literature Rothballer[30] has indicated that male fighting behaviour usually starts at puberty and is correlated with the endocrine cycle. This has been demonstrated in mice quite nicely by Beeman.[31] Male mice usually start to fight at 32 days whereas females hardly fight at all. If, however, the males are castrated at 25 days they remain peaceful until they are injected with male hormone. On the other hand, if adult males who have already started to fight were castrated, they just went on fighting. This suggests some sort of habit formation or learning process, which we shall consider below.

Breeding for Violence

Differential breeding for aggressiveness is possible within any one species. Dogs have long been bred for their temperament. As Scott[6] points out, terriers show so much aggressiveness that, when wire-haired fox terriers were raised together, they started to fight as early as seven or eight weeks old. On the other hand, beagles and cocker spaniels live very peaceably together. Furthermore, in direct aggressive competition for food or for mates, fox terriers beat larger beagles on almost every occasion. Lagerspetz[32] has demonstrated that it is possible to breed albino mice selectively for aggressiveness. The difference in aggressiveness appeared as early as the second generation and did not increase further beyond the seventh generation. As the mice were reared by their natural parents, it was possible that the more aggressive parents in some way taught their offspring to be more aggressive. Lagerspetz controlled for this possibility by cross-fostering experiments in which the offspring of the aggressive parents were reared by the non-aggressive parents and vice versa. The results of this procedure indicated that the aggressive mothers did slightly increase the aggressiveness of their offspring (and noticeable differences in rearing behaviour were discerned), but that this did not mask the genetically controlled variation achieved by the selective breeding.

This experiment illustrates a fundamental point that has to be understood in relation to almost every type of behaviour. There is no either–or dichotomy between nurture (developmental experience) and nature (the inherent genetic equipment). Development is an interactional process between the genetic substrate and the environment. Normal members of the 'higher' animal groups are born with a whole range of genetic potentials that are developed to a greater or lesser extent, left dormant, or distorted by the environment in which the individual finds himself.

Our old friend the rhesus monkey has, in recent years, provided powerful evidence for the importance of nurture in primates. In a now famous series of experiments the Harlows[33] in Wisconsin have shown that if baby rhesus monkeys are deprived of parental care and social contact during an early and crucial stage of their development, they fail to develop the necessary social skills for normal rhesus monkey life. They discovered that maternal deprivation could be compensated for if full peer group interaction with other infant monkeys was allowed but that peer deprivation irreversibly blighted the animal's capacity for social adjustment. The socially deprived monkeys sat in their cages staring fixedly into space, clasped their heads in their hands and rocked for long periods of time. Sometimes they chewed and tore at their own bodies until they bled. At the age of two they showed no normal sexual behaviour; males and females have been kept together in a single cage for as long as seven years without any sexual contact being made, and sometimes they fought so viciously they had to be separated. Mixing these deprived monkeys with normal monkeys in the local zoo produced a lot of fighting, a drowned male, and two injured females, but no improvement in behaviour or any pregnancies. In later work[34] seven of the deprived monkeys were artificially impregnated. All were totally inadequate mothers and none of their infants would have survived if they had not been removed and reared by hand. Three of the 'motherless mothers' did in fact kill their infants. An interesting subsidiary observation from this study was that no matter how much pain the mothers inflicted on their infants, or how many times they would beat them, the little ones would keep coming back for more.

Training

It would be very difficult to substantiate the view that the rhesus monkeys in the Harlow experiments 'learned' to be aggressive—in many ways it could be said that they had failed to learn how not to be aggressive. Boelkins and Heiser[35] have suggested recently that escape and attack are very primitive mammalian social behaviours and that with the evolution of increasingly complex forms of social organisation and social interactions these primitive patterns have been overlaid and suppressed. Certainly there seems to be confirmatory evidence of this view from work with other (non-primate) mammals. Kahn[36] found that mice raised in isolation were somewhat more defensive and strikingly more aggressive and less investigatory than those reared to maturity by their mothers. Eibl-Eibesfeldt[37] raised grey Norway rats in isolation and found that when another rat was introduced into the cage, the isolated rat would attack it with the same patterns of threat and fighting used by experienced animals. In other words, you do not have to teach mammals to fight, they can manage this to some extent as soon as they are physically strong enough. Rather they have to learn how to control their fighting—when to threaten, when to fight and perhaps how to win.

Nevertheless, Scott[38] has come to the conclusion after long experience with fighting experiments in mice that training is a very important aspect of fighting behaviour. He has demonstrated that mice can be trained to fight or trained not to fight, and that once trained in one direction it is difficult to retrain them in the opposite direction. His method of training to fight was to place an inexperienced mouse with an experienced fighter and then, as soon as he began to fight back, the pair were separated so that there was no danger of injury and no chance for the inexperienced mouse to develop the habit of avoidance. The following day another mouse is held by the tail and bumped against the trainee in such a way that he is stimulated to attack. Fighters trained in this way soon become so ferocious that they will even attack females and young, which males ordinarily will not do. Other mice were trained not to fight by caging them with females, which they will not attack, then handling and stroking them and placing them back in the cage so that they came to associate handling with not fighting a cage mate. Two males were each separately treated in this way and then placed together in a pen with one or two females. There was no fighting and peaceful co-existence lasted for some weeks.

Precipitants of Violence

Tread on a dog's foot or tail and it will probably threaten if not actually attack you. Pinch a mouse's tail and it will bite you. These everyday observations demonstrate that pain is a precipitant or trigger for aggressive behaviour in mammals. If rats are standing on a metal floor through which they receive electric shocks, they will fight one another.[39] Moreover they will learn to fight at the sound of a buzzer if the aggression-triggering electric shock is usually accompanied by a buzzer, another form of training.[40] A more interesting and perhaps surprising illustration of the relation of pain to aggression was given in an experiment conducted by Azrin and his colleagues.[41] They found that squirrel monkeys would learn to pull a chain when they were given an electric shock to their tails if that chain produced a canvas ball which they could then attack.

We have already considered overcrowding and a disturbed social situation as other precipitants of fighting. Further possible precipitants worthy of consideration are frustration, shortage of food, and social isolation. Breeding factors, training, and hormonal influences cannot really be considered as precipitants, though they are background or predisposing factors.

At one stage frustration was regarded as an essential precipitant of violence in human beings (see p55). This has never been claimed for animal violence, but there has long been an awareness that a frustrated animal will be more liable to attack than a contented one. Right back in the earliest learning experiments Pavlov[42] noticed that dogs would become aggressive if after they had been trained to give a particular response, they were confined by conflicting or unclear stimuli. In his particular experiments the dogs were given a dish of food at the same time as they saw a large circle, but given no food at the sight of an ellipse. They soon learnt to salivate at the sight of a circle but not at the ellipse. Later Pavlov made the circle slightly elliptical and the ellipse more circular. This process was continued until the dogs could no longer distinguish one from the other. At this point they became 'neurotic', refusing to cooperate further, barking and threatening. Jane Goodall[43] noticed that frustrated young chimpanzees would rock from side to side, scratch their arms, or yawn. Pigeons rewarded by food for correct behaviour will fight one another if that correct behaviour ceases to be rewarded.[44]

In some ways hunger can be regarded as a special form of frustration and we may, therefore, expect it to induce fighting amongst animals. The evidence, however, does not seem to point in this direction. Seward[45] found that hungry rats were less aggressive than well fed ones and in the experiments previously mentioned, carried out by Southwick[26] at Calcutta Zoo, it was found that while reduction of space and the introduction of newcomers both produced outbreaks of violence, a 25 per cent food reduction resulted in no change in the amount of agonistic interaction. A 50 per cent food reduction actually decreased the number of agonistic encounters and the monkeys became lethargic. This kind of result has also been found in human work and was used by the Nazis during World War II as a means of controlling large camps of imprisoned people with a small number of guards.

Keys and his colleagues,[46] who have looked into the effects of starvation upon humans, confirm that it is accompanied by depression, lethargy, languor and immobility; but they urge us to distinguish actual food reduction from threatened food reduction. The latter, they maintain, produces aggression and irritability. This hypothesis is confirmed among rhesus monkeys in the Calcutta Zoo experiments, since Southwick found that when the food supply was not reduced but unevenly distributed by placing it all in one basket, there was an increase in the fighting.

Functions of Violence

The preceeding few pages should have made it clear that aggression is very common, almost universal, among mammals, certainly among primates. Indeed it is probably not going too far to say that aggression, with violence at one end of the spectrum, is an essential component of mammalian life. From an evolutionary point of view this implies a function for aggression, because purposeless redundant behaviour is likely to disappear in preference to behaviour that assists the species in its struggle for survival. What then are the functions of violence?

The first function may well be the one which Darwin highlighted and related to his underlying rule of biology, that the fittest and strongest survive and the weakest do not live very long or produce many descendants. Certainly in the few examples we have examined in this chapter it seems that aggression and violence determine who gets the first choice of food and of sexual partner, and that dominant or aggressive groups have more room to manoeuvre or develop than non-aggressive groups.

Related to this perhaps slightly old-fashioned evolutionary view is the notion that aggression and violence may spread animals apart so that natural resources are shared and feeding can take place over a wider area.

Perhaps it is not without significance that some of the most successful creatures are both social and yet aggressive to their own kind. Why do we live in groups in the first place? Animals that are entirely solitary are at a great disadvantage when it comes to defence, since they have to rely entirely upon their own resources. There can be no division of labour, such as one individual keeping a watch for predators while others feed or sleep. In groups relatively helpless creatures can put up a reasonable defence against a powerful foe, as anyone who has ever witnessed a group of small birds mobbing a cat can testify. Baboons also can cope with leopards and lions by feeding in groups, the stronger males remaining on the periphery of the group and never allowing any one individual to become isolated. This type of group defence was presumably a prerequisite in their development because their ancestors were entirely tree creatures, but now they can leave the protection of trees and move into open savannah to eat a wide variety of foodstuffs.

Another distinct advantage of group living is that infants can spend some of their life in an immature phase during which they have to be protected and nurtured by the adult members of the group. A young baboon, for example, lives some 12–24 months before he is fully able to take care of himself.[23] This long immature phase gives an enormous opportunity for learning and for picking up the essential elements of successful living from the surrounding experienced adults. Only creatures with a long immature developmental phase can be sure that the new generation will have a chance quickly to adapt to a changing environment. It is the opportunity to adapt via this learning phase which Washburn and Hamburg have suggested is the fundamental *raison d'etre* of the social group. 'It is in the group that experience is pooled and the generations linked. The adaptive function of prolonged biological youth is that it gives the animal time to learn. During this period while the animal learns from other members of the group it is protected by them.'[47]

Groups function best when they have a common purpose, when there is central leadership. A leader with obedient subordinates can produce an orderly concerted approach to a problem whether it be a threat from another species, from a similar rival group, or from the inanimate environment itself. This is the type of group we find in the primates—a hierarchical group. Aggression with occasional violence or the threat of violence to support it seems to be the mechanism that has developed to produce such a hierarchical structure, and it may be central to the regulation and control of the social group.

References to this chapter appear on pp181-3

3 *Violent Mechanisms*

If the reader has gained the impression from the previous chapter that all animals are violent, this is erroneous. Fairly obvious examples of non-aggressive creatures (remembering that in this book we are only dealing with intra-species aggression—conflict between members of the same species) are caterpillars and butterflies, earthworms, mussels, and barnacles. What then is the difference between these animals and those that are aggressors? One basic difference is that the creatures listed do not really have any mechanism for fighting. Aggression is a meaningless concept unless there is the possibility of a real destructive force being brought into play. Earthworms, butterflies and the like do not fight largely because they cannot fight. What is man's fighting machine and how did he get it?

Evolution of Violence

One of the earliest writers to theorise about behavioural evolution was Carveth Read[13], who noted that all our primate relatives live on a largely fruit or vegetable diet, whereas man is omnivorous, that is, he eats a large proportion of meat in his diet. More than that, he is a hunter—he actively sets out to catch and kill prey in the same way that the big cats or wolves do. Read suggested, therefore, that for dietary purposes the pre-hominids became wolf-like primates, hunting in packs, and that this new carnivorous or hunting element in their behaviour gave them the advantage that they could get away from the fruit trees and explore the plains, and it also led them to become more aggressive and more cooperative than their fructiverous ancestors. Several contemporary writers have also taken up this theme. Tiger[2] has suggested that the need for cooperation in hunting led to a behavioural divergence between males and females: males developed special bonds among themselves through going away from home base in groups, while females specialised in maternal and gathering activities at the home base. He further believes that the catching and killing skills, singly or in groups, were later transferred to conflicts between men.

This viewpoint has, however, a fundamental weakness that has already been mentioned. Herbivorous primates such as rhesus monkeys and baboons can also be very violent—Zuckerman's Hamadryas Baboons[22] had no heritage as hunters to produce the slaughter he witnessed. Leakey[48] is another advocate of the hunter thesis, but he forestalls part of the objection just expressed by suggesting that man was first a scavenger, just as chimpanzees or baboons can scavenge today, and that he competed against primate scavengers by threatening or fighting them. Having learnt to threaten and attack other primates, it was just a short step to threatening or attacking other men. Unfortunately this proposition still does not account for the intra-specific violence of herbivorous creatures. Even so, it should not be discarded entirely, for we have to take note of the remarkable propensity for man to regard other men as lower animals and vice versa (see p61) and of the cannibalistic trait that crops up in some human cultures. It seems to me that we have to go a lot further back in evolution than primates for an answer. To restate an evolutionary truism, intra-specific violence and aggression are widespread among animals with backbones and it is, therefore, probably of advantage to them. The functions of aggression and its advantages have already been examined (p34). Such advantages would produce selection pressures so that the more aggressive creatures would be the more successful and so survive better as a species.

To recapitulate, it should be remembered that most of the advantages of aggression are to be found in the social life of the animal concerned, and it is in the development of a complex social life that the primates have developed their particular adaptation to their environment. Man is spectacularly successful in his conquest of the environment (which now embraces the whole globe and could even include other parts of the solar system); he has left the shelter of the trees and gone out into the open savannah and become carnivorous. To become carnivorous he needed to add to his armamentarium, which is basically very scanty, by learning to make tools and artificial weapons, and he needed to cooperate.

In a recent book Bigelow[49] has argued that man's evolution has been dependent upon a combination of extreme ferocity with extreme cooperativeness. He believes that early hominids competed fiercely with one another and group attacked group. The ones with the best degree of cooperation, with the best brains in fact (for he sees cooperativeness as very much a function of intelligence and brainpower) were the most successful in these conflicts. Hence the ordinary evolutionary process of survival of the fittest produced a cooperative, intelligent large-brained animal as an offshoot of his ferocity. Unfortunately this thesis does not explain where the ferocity came from in the first place, or why other species have not also used this evolutionary route. Nevertheless, it acknowledges the intimate connection between success in warfare and cooperativeness, and suggests an evolutionary reason for modern man's preoccupation with warfare. Which came first we cannot be sure, but there seems no doubt that group cooperativeness was (and is) essential for survival to the hominids. It is probably no accident that man, the most 'successful' species to inhabit the earth so far, is also the most gregarious. As with

all other species, man has found that this cooperativeness depends upon bonding and its antithesis—aggression. No creature can live in close association with another without the
closeness and the personal rights of each one being limited in
some way. These limits are set by the attractive and repellent
forces between them—bonds and aggression, love and hate.
Man's bonds and anti-bonds are highly developed.

Differences between Man and Other Species

I have already side-stepped the 'which species is more aggressive' argument, but if we are to examine the mechanism of
violence in man, perhaps we can with advantage consider some
of the differences between his behaviour and that of other
modern species. I would like to suggest that there are five
main differences between human violence and animal violence: (1) it is more intelligently applied, (2) there are special
and subtle psychological mechanisms available to man which
colour, or alter, the violence in some situations, (3) group
violence shows a marked degree of cooperativeness, (4) tools
are effectively used, and (5) some of the inhibitory mechanisms that many species use to prevent bloodshed in agonistic
encounters are either weakly developed in man or frequently
rendered ineffective by other mechanisms.

The psychological mechanisms used by man in aggression
and violence are given in Chapter 4. Intelligence, however, is
not included there and should be briefly considered now. It is
exceedingly difficult to give a precise definition of intelligence,
but for our purposes we can consider it as the ability to solve
problems, to memorise events and to communicate with others
of the same species. Obviously the faster, more completely,
these tasks are carried out, the higher the intelligence is
deemed to be. Aggression is the process of 'winning' against
another individual, of taking from him, or retaining against
his efforts to regain it a piece of territory, a partner, food and
so forth. Inevitably, in achieving these objectives, man has
developed more and more subtle, ingenious or effective ways

of winning. Some of these types of aggression include violence, and here we must include toolmaking as an intelligent aid to violence (see below). Language is one of man's unique and greatest achievements, and it, too, plays its part in aggressive interactions. Washburn[50] has suggested that man is less aggressive than other creatures simply because he can communicate his demands more easily by language and because he can develop a system of winning and losing, of dominance and submission, within the language structure without clenching his fists or baring his teeth as a dumb hominid would have to do; and there can be no doubt that language is used for aggressive purposes and speech can be violent in producing submission and psychological damage. When we come to consider the control of violence in Chapter 9, we shall see that, on the whole, formalised verbal battles are preferred to physical assaults, and that for large-scale group interactions we are trying, with varying degrees of success, to develop these techniques.

The cooperativeness of group violence which we shall look at in more detail later is really just an extension of the cooperativeness seen in a multitude of human activities. Furthermore, it is just an extension of what is already seen in other primates: for instance, Southwick and his colleagues[19] saw a small group of rhesus monkeys involved in a fight, and as soon as other members of the group saw what was happening or heard the cries of their fellows, they joined in to chase off the common enemy.

Many forms of human violence are utterly dependent upon the high level of cooperativeness that man exhibits. War is the obvious example. To conduct a battle successfully a hierarchy has to be developed and adhered to, and instructions from a commander carried out even when they fly in the face of reason or other emotions. The famous British charge of the Light Brigade during the Crimean War illustrates the degree of submission that can be involved (for a discussion of obedience, see p69); moreover marked division of labour is required, some individuals learning one skill and some another, and yet all pooling their resources for a common purpose. No rhesus monkey battle could last for more than a few hours, since the monkeys would get tired and hungry and give up. In fact, war is dependent upon marked cooperativeness and a high degree of intelligence, which is probably the reason why man is the only mammal to indulge in it. He is the only one equipped to do so.

This does not mean war is unique to man—it is not, for ants also indulge.[25] Once again, however, we see an animal that possesses a marked degree of cooperativeness and a striking degree of division of labour. Ants run supply lines, bring up reinforcements and the like not by intelligence but through intuitive responses that are almost certainly not modifiable by learning processes. These may have taken something in excess of 50 million years to evolve.[51] The point is, however, that ants have mechanisms available for war, just like man.

Artificial tools are, however, almost unique to man. It is true that Jane Goodall[52] has seen chimpanzees making instruments to extract termites from a hill, and that on occasions they throw things at one another or at humans, but these are very different from the complex and sophisticated weapons that even the early hominids used. No one can be sure whether weapons were first used for predation or for violence or both simultaneously. Intelligent man has now reached the point where he has destructive tools that can eliminate either all or the majority of his own species at one fell swoop, a point of enormous significance in the evolution of man and part explanation for all the current interest in violence. For all the horrors of the past, man has never before shown such an interest in intra-specific aggression. It is a very reasonable interest, as he may never get the opportunity to reflect on it again.

Some have maintained that weapons are the only basic difference in violent behaviour between man and other primates. This is not quite correct, for, as we have already indicated, there are differences in the degree of cooperation and we shall discuss below differences in inhibitory control. There is no doubt at all, however, that weapons are a fundamental aspect of contemporary human violence. Once an intelligent competitive being learns that it can defeat a fellow by threatening or attacking him with a weapon slightly better than anything his adversary possesses, then the arms race is on. Just consider for a moment how ill-equipped man is when he has to fight without weapons. It is extremely difficult for one naked unarmed man to kill another such man. He has to resort to strangulation, or to punching him hard enough to knock him over so that he may gash an important blood vessel open with his teeth, or break his head open by dashing it against the ground. Revolting, isn't it? Quite so, and few of us would be prepared or, for that matter, capable of killing another person if we had to do it this way, but give us a few weapons, even some clothing, and the scene changes. Clubs, ropes, swords, pistols, nuclear bombs, all greatly facilitate our task. Many who could just be bruised in unarmed combat are, by means of weapons, seriously injured or killed. Weapons magnify the aggressivity of a creature many times.

Not surprisingly then, when we come to consider methods of controlling violence (Chapter 9), we shall look carefully to see if there are ways of controlling weapons, since the fewer the weapons the less the violence. It is probably no coincidence that the United States, which has a high murder rate and a serious problem of violent robberies in some of its big cities, also has, for historical reasons, an enormous cache of firearms spread throughout the houses of ordinary citizens. 'Muggings' in the street, bank holdups, and even violent rows in the home take on an altogether different complexion if loaded firearms are available.

Anti-violence Mechanisms

It has already been mentioned (Chapter 2) how ethologists have noticed that, when two animals are fighting, a submission posture in one—the loser—indicates the end of the struggle. The animal may cower, crouch down, bow, or flee, and the assault or impending assault is inhibited. Clearly this is a useful protective mechanism as far as the species is concerned, for it allows aggressive encounters to take place and winners to be decided without causing physical damage to individuals. Even so, there are occasions when the inhibitory mechanisms do not work—Zuckerman's monkey hill[22] is a good example of that. Man has a number of self-protective submissive postures that can either lubricate social encounters or in fighting save life —bowing, kneeling, hands placed together in front of the body, hands raised above the head. Once again these do not always work and, in spite of marked submission behaviour, some victims are cruelly done to death by their adversaries. Some writers suggest that only man habitually disregards these submission postures,[53] but the Zuckerman work and the Southwick studies[21] show that this is not strictly true; a great deal depends upon the situation a particular animal finds himself in. Eibl-Eibesfeldt[54] has suggested that one of the crucial determinants of the power of an inhibitory act is the violence potential of the species concerned. Very dangerous animals (eg, rattlesnakes) never bite each other, presumably because the outcome would be disastrous. Wolves that do bite one another nevertheless have submission postures that are strongly inhibitory. Only animals without weapons or animals that can retreat easily have no such social inhibitions. In the wild, hamsters bite each other viciously, but once bitten the loser quickly retreats and the winner does not chase it to destruction. In captivity, however, hamsters will kill one another because they cannot protect themselves by running away. Perhaps, therefore, because he is naked, unarmed man is not very dangerous and hence has not evolved very powerful submission mechanisms. Maybe this is an example of our accelerated social evolution leaving our genetic evolution far behind.

When we were thinking about tools, I suggested that the spectacle or thought of killing another man with our bare hands would revolt most of us. In fact, most of us could just not bring ourselves to do it. Weapons enable us to overcome these inhibitions. They produce 'clean' instead of revolting death. Furthermore, as Lorenz has suggested,[54] modern weapons can act so quickly that the victim has no opportunity to surrender or submit. Technology has brought us to the point where now we can kill other people by remote control and in comfort—by bombing, missiles, or rockets. In these conditions no inhibitory mechanisms, however powerful, would have the chance to operate.

Brain Mechanisms

Up to now the importance of learning for the higher mammals and primates has been stressed, but we must not forget the importance of the underlying structure of the animal concerned. The physical inheritance of the animal sets the limits to which it can be trained. As we have already seen, some creatures, like ants, are born with a very limited learning capacity, and early experiences do not condition and mould their final behavioural pattern. It is the reverse with *homo sapiens*, who is born with enormous potential that has to be developed by learning. If he were not given the potential to speak, to read, to write, no amount of training could produce these characteristics—chimpanzees can never be taught any of them. His environmental experiences determine whether he will learn any or all of them and which particular language he will communicate in. Similarly, a primate cannot be violent without the physical substrate which is necessary for violence.

The basic control system for any animal's behaviour is its nervous system. Man, with his enormously complicated repertoire of behaviour, has the most elaborately complicated nervous system currently known. Much of our knowledge of the function and structure of our brain comes from a detailed assessment of the brains of other creatures, especially mammals. Fortunately, this is no handicap, because the similarities of function between some aspects of human brains and the brains of other mammals are very considerable. It is impossible to deal with the complexities of neuro-anatomy and neuro-physiology in any detail here and the interested reader is referred to the more specialised volumes listed in the References. A particularly helpful short article, which has provided the basis of much of what follows, is 'Brain Mechanisms Related to Aggressive Behaviour' by Birger Kaada of Oslo.[55] A very simplistic view of the human brain is given in the adjacent drawing, which is a diagrammatic section roughly taken down the middle of an adult head and neck. Most of the structures are indicated but for the purist it should be noted

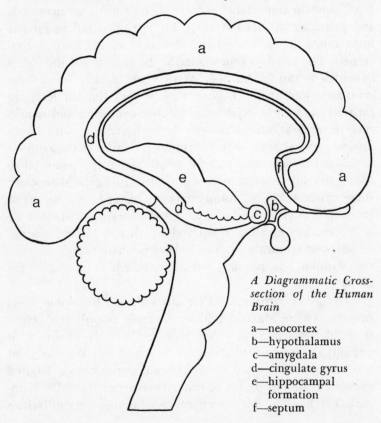

A Diagrammatic Cross-section of the Human Brain

a—neocortex
b—hypothalamus
c—amygdala
d—cingulate gyrus
e—hippocampal
     formation
f—septum

that in life they do not all lie on the same plane, as is shown by this two-dimensional drawing.

For many years it has been known that if all the structures a, c, d, e, and f are removed, leaving only the brain stem and spinal column, an animal can continue to live but a state of irritability known as 'sham rage' sets in. Any stimulus given to such a 'decorticate' cat, such as stroking it, makes it hiss, growl, arch its back and sometimes strike out in a most ferocious way. Various neuro-physiologists have suggested that the phenomenon is due to the release of higher inhibitory or restraining mechanisms on the hypothalamus. There is an area of the hypothalamus which when destroyed produces a complete loss of emotional responsiveness, with a mask-like face, reduced vocalisation, general inactivity, and stolidity. Today neuro-surgery has advanced to the point where minute electrodes can be placed in a defined area of an animal's (or a man's) brain and stimulated by electrical wires or even more remotely by means of radio waves which the subject receives through a special receiver. Stimulation experiments of this kind have led some researchers to try and define particular areas of the hypothalamus as being responsible for 'aggression' and others for 'flight'. It is also possible, as Kaada[55] suggests, that in the cat there are slightly different areas controlling agression or defensive behaviour and the stalking of prey. However, it should not be thought that there is a simple push-button area arrangement for triggering particular types of aggressive behaviour in the hypothalamus. Workers still disagree about the exact location and function of any one area, integration and co-ordination of various parts of the nervous system being probably more important than any one area of itself, and Masserman[56] has concluded that responses artificially induced in the hypothalamus have no meaning for the animal—a cat engaged in eating or grooming would strike out in apparent anger when his hypothalamus was stimulated but would resume what he was doing when the current was turned off as though nothing had happened.

If the suggestion that sham rage is due to an absence of cortical inhibition is correct, the cerebral cortex is clearly an important structure in the control of violence. The part of the brain that is particularly well developed in man and is probably responsible for much of our 'intelligence' is called the neocortex (because it evolved quite recently). In some famous experiments carried out by Bard and Mountcastle, again on cats, it was found that 'placidity' or an extreme refractoriness to annoying stimuli was produced by extensive removal of the neocortex, provided the 'older' cortical structures known as the limbic system (the amygdala, cingulate gyrus, hippocampal formation, septum) were preserved. This suggests perhaps that the neocortex normally exerts some kind of excitatory effect in an aggressive situation, although as the cats were also blind and deaf we may be noticing the effect of a loss of sensory input.

Conversely, if the structures of the limbic system were damaged, a state of persistent and extreme ferocity was produced. Unfortunately, just to add confusion to the picture, other workers have not been able to reproduce these experiments.[55] Indeed many other workers have obtained directly conflicting results: for example, Kluver and Bucy[57] in a very famous experiment removed both temporal lobes, including the amygdala and the greater part of the hippocampus, from rhesus monkeys and found a number of very strange behavioural reactions, including a seeming reduction of anger and fear. Whatever the exact details of the neuro-physiology, it is now clear that the limbic system, especially the amygdala, is an essential component in the normal aggression mechanism. In general, if both amygdalae are removed or destroyed, there is an increased tameness or placidity for the animal concerned. Some authorities are now advocating this as a neuro-surgical operation in some especially aggressive men (p109). Another part of the limbic system involved in aggressive behaviour is the septum. Destruction of this area causes an increase in aggressiveness,[55] but this increase is removed completely and suddenly by amygdalectomy (removal of the amygdala).

These then are some of the neurological structures involved in aggressive behaviour—the hypothalamus, the neocortex, and the limbic system (with its hippocampus, amygdala and septum). However, as I have already suggested, to regard them as isolated centres is illogical, as they undoubtedly form a co-ordinated network of nervous control. Similarly, it is fallacious to consider these internal mechanisms entirely without reference to the outside environment and the stimuli the mechanisms are having to deal with. Brown and Hunsperger[58] have emphasised this point and have pointed out that the nervous mechanism in the cat for threat behaviour overlaps with that for escape behaviour. The exact outcome of stimulation may well depend upon the nature and intensity of the stimulus received rather than on the particular organ stimulated.

Very few researchers have actually studied the results of particular stimulation and ablation experiments in relation to an organised social situation. One of these was Rosvold and his colleagues[59] who put eight rhesus monkeys together until a dominance hierarchy had been established; the three most dominant ones then had bilateral amygdalectomies, whereupon two of these three fell to the bottom of the hierarchy because they became less aggressive whereas the third, who became more aggressive, retained his position. Jose Delgado and his colleagues at Yale have put special emphasis on these social effects in this type of experiment. They have undertaken a series of studies in which animals (usually rhesus monkeys) have been fitted with electrodes implanted in various known parts of their brains and have had these electrodes stimulated remotely by radio control. One monkey (a female) had the same area of brain (the right cerebellar peduncle) stimulated in different social situations. When restrained in a chair she became restless, made high-pitched noises and rotated her eyes and head. When free in a cage, much the same occurred; she also ran across the cage and launched attacks on a low-ranking monkey. In the presence of a superior monkey no threatening took place.[60]

Delgado[61] has also given a remarkable demonstration of rhesus monkeys learning to use a technology they had not been clever enough to invent. In some of his experiments he demonstrated that the aggressivity and hence the authority of boss monkeys increased when the posteromedial nucleus of the thalamus (just above the hypothalamus in the diagram) was stimulated and, conversely, their authority diminished when another part of the thalamus (the caudate nucleus) was stimulated because some of their aggressive activity was inhibited. Subordinate monkeys learned to stimulate the caudate nucleus by remote control with a lever as they quickly noticed that pressing the lever inhibited the superior monkey's aggressiveness. Animal farm come true? I wonder what the result would have been if the monkeys could have used a trigger lever which fired dangerous missiles at other monkeys?

Physiology of Aggression

When an animal is asleep or quietly digesting a meal, it is not really very well equipped for fighting or for running away if attacked. The heart and circulation are just ticking over sufficiently to keep the vital organs alive, and if digestion is taking place in the gut, extra supplies of blood are shunted in that direction. Should an aggressive response become suddenly necessary large quantities of energy have to be mobilised, the heart has to pump blood much faster and more powerfully, the lungs have to ventilate more rapidly, and the muscles, which will do the work, require massive blood supplies to bring them the food and oxygen that is about to be needed. Clearly a sensitive and rapid means is required to regulate this kind of fundamental change. The system used is a hormonal one, that is, a chemical one. When the brain takes the decision to fight, it sends out appropriate messages which, in turn, cause particular glands to secrete chemicals (hormones) that circulate in the blood stream and alter the internal physiology to what is required.

The adrenal glands, which sit on top of the kidneys in the abdomen, are of special importance in this mechanism. The middle part of the gland produces adrenaline and noradrenaline, which increase the heart rate and push up its pressure, and direct blood from the gut to the muscles. The outside or cortical part of the gland produces a series of adrenocortical hormones, such as aldosterone and cortisone. These mobilise stores of energy in the body and feed muscles by providing a raised blood sugar; they keep, by means of complex chemical changes, the muscles strong and in a condition to contract powerfully, and they are concerned with combating drowsiness and fatigue. Clearly then this series of mechanisms provides an essential background to aggressive behaviour.

Another effect of being aroused to fight or flight in this way is an increase in sweating of the skin. In recent years techniques have been developed to measure the patterns of palmar sweating, pulse rate, and forearm blood flow (which indicates the volume of blood going to the forearm muscles). Some researchers have suggested that people who are abnormally aggressive—the so-called psychopaths (see p114)—have abnormalities in these physiological features that distinguish them from other people.[62] This is an area of considerable experimental difficulty, however, and the results are far from being generally accepted.

Sex Hormones

We saw from Chapter 2 that in every species of mammal the males are more aggressive than the females. Human beings are mammals and this rule applies to them. In spite of what some contemporary writers would have us believe, there are basic differences in behaviour between male and female humans that transcend any minor cultural habits that may have recently and perhaps transiently developed. Tiger[2] discusses these in some detail in a recent book, but there is no doubt that aggressiveness and violence are especially related to maleness. Female soldiers are unusual and it is even more unusual for female soldiers to carry out battle duties or actually become embroiled in the violence of a war. Where they do so, they usually belong to a struggling group (eg, guerrillas) desperately throwing all resources into the actual fighting. Many cultures do not use women at all in their police services. Countries that do this, like Britain, use them in a different role from their male policemen—they are much less often used in violent situations and even then it is usually only against violent females. Women figure much less prominently in crime statistics, including violent crime statistics, than do men. Female boxers and wrestlers are rare.

Perhaps this just indicates that traditions have prescribed different roles for the sexes. This is partly true, but these traditions have developed from physical differences. Sexual behaviour is related to and partly dependent upon the presence of circulating hormones, oestrogens in females and testosterone in males. Castrated men, like castrated bulls, have little or no interest in sexual activities—this fact has been used as a form of social control against sexual deviance in some countries (especially Denmark). However, this is not tantamount to saying that sexual behaviour is *entirely* dependent upon sexual hormones, nor that it is *directly* related to the level of circulating hormone. Being associated with maleness, aggressiveness is also somewhat related to sexual hormones. The farmer does not castrate the young bull just to keep him away from the cows, he wants him to be a docile amenable working animal. Some mammals do, in fact, show marked physical differentiation between the sexes which is related to differences in aggressivity. The male baboon, for example, is bigger and much fiercer looking than the female. Although men and women are rather similar in naked appearance, there are, nevertheless, a number of specially masculine characteristics hormonally determined, which are related to aggressiveness—extra height, stronger muscles, bearded (and more frightening) face, and faster running speeds.

References to this chapter appear on pp183-4

4 *Psychology of Violence*

This chapter will examine what mental factors, other than those of disease, which will be considered in Chapter 7, are associated with violent behaviour. It will not go into the details of 'the instinct controversy'. A deep and insoluble argument has broken out between, on the one hand, psychoanalysts and some ethologists such as Lorenz[5] who claim that aggression is related to an 'instinct', and some of the more behaviouristic biologists such as Scott[6] and Montagu, on the other hand, who claim that aggression is always provoked by the environment. Montagu has even gone to the trouble to edit a whole book[63] refuting Lorenz's claims about instinct. The instinct school seem to be claiming that aggression is a spontaneous innate drive that slowly builds up like water in a tank and must be released by one route or another. The opposing school views aggression as requiring some sort of stimulus without which peace and tranquillity would reign, presumably for ever. Hinde[7] has neatly reviewed the problem and pointed out the semantic difficulties. Instinct, for example, is used in two ways, sometimes to describe an internal driving force, sometimes to indicate a lack of environmental influence and development. He rightly chides all who become embroiled in these arguments for implying that behaviour can be regarded as *either* learnt *or* innate. Nobody seriously believes these are exclusive alternatives, except in extreme cases; in fact the study of behaviour soon leads to interaction hypotheses involving a number of different factors, and in higher mammals we are often concerned with an inherited potential developed or triggered to a greater or lesser extent by a particular environment.

This book will try and stick to an interaction model, neither discounting environmental influences, whether remote or immediate, nor inner potentials that are based upon a particular anatomy and physiology.

Frustration

'He made me so mad I could have hit him,' is the cry of the frustrated. An important school of psychology developed in the 1930s and 1940s around Dollard and his co-workers,[64] who boldly began their monograph by stating: 'This study takes as its point of departure the assumption that *aggression is always a consequence of frustration*' (my italics). They went further to suggest that aggressive behaviour always presupposes the existence of frustration and, vice versa, the existence of frustration always leads to some form of aggression. Since they based their views on Freudian theory, they were not saying that frustration always leads to violence, for other forms of aggression are equally possible—humour, ridicule, etc. They believed that the strength of the aggressive drive varied directly with the amount of frustration, and the amount of frustration depended upon the strength of the original drive, the degree of interference with that drive and the number of times it was frustrated. Most of the aggression produced, they suggested, is directed against the frustrator, but they accepted the Freudian psychoanalytic notion that the direction of a drive can be altered, eg, by displacement on to an innocent bystander, rather like monkeys who when attacked chase a lower-ranking animal. They quote the example of a normally meek girl who inexplicably let off at a porter who failed to have the exact change ready when she wanted it: that particular morning she had had a severely exasperating experience with her landlord but had managed to inhibit all her aggressive feelings towards him.

Ordinary experience tells us that frustration is an important factor in making us angry and perhaps behaving violently. Anyone in a hurry who has sat in a traffic jam will have noticed how difficult it is to avoid angry, even violent thoughts. Watch how aggressively and dangerously the drivers behave as they drive away from the jam. Relatively simple experiments can be devised to demonstrate these effects in a quantitative way. Sears, Hovland and Miller[65] induced some volunteers to stay up all night in what the subjects thought would be a sleep deprivation experiment. They were promised food, amusements, and cigarettes, but none of these things materialised, and in their frustration the subjects became angry. One took to drawing pictures of violence—hangings, disembowelling and so on, and he made no secret of the fact that the victims were meant to be psychologists. All the subjects enjoyed the 'joke'.

Most workers these days, however, would not go all the way with Dollard and his colleagues. Some frustrating situations do not produce aggression; even more important, not all people acting aggressively or violently are frustrated. Consider the soldier in a foreign land shooting down his enemy either in self-protection or as a result of instructions. Frustration must be given an important place in our understanding of violence, but it is not the only factor involved.

Anger

Anger or 'hot displeasure' as the dictionary calls it is regarded by Rycroft in his *Critical Dictionary of Psychoanalysis*[66] as a 'primary emotion', one that is typically provoked by frustration. Rycroft asks us not to confuse it with hate, which is a much longer-lasting sentiment. In other words anger is a short-lived feeling that often accompanies frustration and, indeed, often accompanies aggression and violence. It may be the way in which we consciously recognise that the structural mechanisms we discussed in Chapter 3 are functioning. Anger and aggression are so intertwined that sometimes we are tempted to use them synonymously, but it should not be forgotten that it is possible for an angry man to inhibit all his aggressive behaviour, and not all violence is associated with anger. Think of the soldier again.

Hatred

We have already seen that primates in general and man in particular are gregarious creatures. To live in groups it is necessary for attractions—or bonds, as biologists call them—to be set up between the members of the group. Positive bond feelings towards others are pleasant and we seek them; we call them love, friendship, affection, fondness. As with any attractive force, however, there is an opposing or negative force—magnetism brings pieces of iron together but it can also send them flying apart. If individuals are attracted together in one group, characteristics that do not belong to that group (the in-group), must, therefore, belong to 'them' (the out-group). It is on this basis that hatred is built.

Hatred can best be regarded as the opposite of love, but it should be distinguished from anger, which is an ephemeral passing emotion. It is quite possible, indeed almost certain, that a person will sometimes be angry with a loved one. Hatred, however, is a persistent feeling, a sentiment that can be extended to a whole group or class of people. At root it is a very violent feeling because it is a wish to injure or destroy. Fromm[67] asks us to distinguish between rational hatred and character-conditioned hatred. The former is a biological defence against real attack in the same way that love is essential for group cohesion; the latter is based upon the mechanisms we shall shortly consider—projection, paranoia, prejudice.

Mental Mechanisms

Powerful feelings like love, hatred, anger and so on are some-

times dealt with by our minds in the simple obvious way, but
because of the complex group system we live in this would not
always be appropriate if both we and the group are to survive.
If we hate our parents or are extremely angry with a colleague,
it is not helpful or effective to cope with the situation by
naked violence; we have to re-route, even distort our feelings
until they are socially acceptable. Psychoanalysis has explored
the mental mechanisms we use to do this, sometimes more
effectively, sometimes less effectively. We have already been
introduced to 'displacement' in the section on frustration. We
saw that a frustrated drive could lead to aggression not necessarily directed at the frustrator. Similarly anger or aggression
generated more internally, for example, by guilt relating to
an important omission or commission can be displaced on to
some sort of scapegoat. A man forgets to bring his wife some
flowers on their wedding anniversary, which omission makes
him feel guilty, bad, worthy of attack; but instead of attacking himself he attacks the children or the dog. Psychoanalytic
theory also teaches us about 'sublimation', a process by which
energy, in this case aggressive energy, is transformed into a
more acceptable form before it is discharged. Somebody who
is basically very angry with his frustrating situation may,
instead of discharging that anger in violence, 'attack' a job
of work, even create a work of art. Anna Freud[68] lists ten
different defence mechanisms of this kind. The others most
relevant to the study of aggression are 'repression' (the girl
in the story quoted above would be said to be repressing
or inhibiting her anger until it was displaced on to the
porter); 'reaction-formation', an unacceptable feeling which
is mastered by exaggeration of the opposing tendency, so that
solicitude may be a reaction-formation against cruelty;[4] 'turning against the self' (an analytic explanation for suicidal
behaviour); and 'projection'.

Projection is a particularly important mechanism because
it underlies another key phenomenon in the psychology of
violence—'paranoia'. Rycroft[66] defines projection as the pro-

cess by which impulses and wishes are imagined to be located in some object external to oneself. A thought that is unpleasant (eg, an aggressive thought) is defended or made acceptable to the self-esteem by asserting that someone else has it (denial)—I don't hate X but Y does hate him. More often it is accompanied by 'reversal'—I don't hate X, X hates me.

Paranoia

Paranoia is a feeling of being persecuted or got at. It is almost universal in some degree, and it is a very important component of quarrels, murders, wars, etc, because those who feel persecuted are likely to try and defend themselves against the assumed enemy.

In his original thinking Freud[69] interpreted all paranoid ideas as related to sexuality—especially homosexuality. The unacceptable feeling of 'I love him' was supposedly transformed into 'I hate him' and then reversed to 'he hates me', which at last became acceptable. Few writers agree with this view today and in his later writings Freud himself[70] accepted the notion of aggressive feelings independent of sexual feelings. Melanie Klein,[71] a later psychoanalyst, has elaborated a theory of paranoia more fully. She assumes that there is an innate conflict between love and hate in every baby, which is present from the moment of birth and which has a constitutional basis. In her view every individual has a greedy and hostile component to his nature, and if his psychological development is not complete, he may deal with these unacceptable feelings by attributing them to other people: 'I am aggressive' becomes 'he is aggressive'. In other words the anxiety of hate is dealt with by projecting it on to another person.

Whatever the basis for paranoia, it undoubtedly plays a central role in some forms of violent behaviour. It is perhaps not surprising that anyone in a frustrating situation feels slightly paranoid. When the frustrator is impersonal, or difficult to locate, it seems helpful to the mind to personalise him so that a target for retaliative aggression can be formed. Remember the rats who were shocked. They were not to know the nature of their real persecutor and in any case they could not get at him; so they attacked one another. In the southern states of the USA lynchings of negroes were related to the business cycle: [72] when cotton prices were low and crops could not be sold, the frustrated white farmers felt persecuted and displaced their aggression on to the negroes. Feelings of persecution can reach delusional level. A paranoid individual can believe in the face of contrary evidence and with unshakeable conviction that a particular person is persecuting him and must, therefore, be eliminated. Paranoid thoughts are not confined to individuals. Groups, indeed whole nations, can hold them. Racism is based on paranoid ideas. 'Things are not as we want them—someone is responsible for the mess we are in—it can't be us, that is too threatening an idea, it would only confirm our fears of inadequacy—it must be *them*.' Any 'them' will do but preferably an identifiable 'them'—badges, such as hairstyles and clothes will indicate a 'them', as will religion, and, best of all, something permanent like a dark skin or a Semitic nose.

We will return to the question of group paranoia when we consider wars, but just for the moment let us ponder on the beliefs held by the super-powers in current international politics. Both the USSR and the USA have the nuclear capability of destroying each other, both feel that they are surrounded by weapons belonging to the other side, and both feel that the other side is unfriendly and wishes them harm. The danger of this situation is that one or the other side may feel so threatened that it will feel obliged to strike first.

Prejudice

When we project our problems on to 'them' and blame 'them' for our misfortunes, we are being guilty of prejudice. It can be defined as 'thinking ill of others without sufficient warrant'.[73] Allport sees part of the explanation in our power-ful tendency to form in-groups and out-groups. We have already seen that other species do this—a stranger cannot be introduced safely to a rat colony. Being very dependent on each other for our very existence, we form groups. Our posi-tive feelings to our group are very strong and induce beliefs that our group is a 'good' group—my family, my team, my firm, my country—all good, therefore I am good. The con-verse of an in-group like this must necessarily be an out-group that is not so good—not worth belonging to, because it is the alternative to mine. An out-group is an obvious target for paranoid projection, for prejudice. It becomes the 'them' just mentioned.

Allport went on to suggest that people develop a generalised prejudiced set or a 'prejudiced personality', which, in descrip-tive terms, is characterised by an ambivalence towards the person's parents, a rigidly moralistic view of life, a need to divide the world into good and bad categories, a need to remove doubt and be definite, a lack of self-insight or under-standing, a love of order, especially social order and social institutions (eg, lodges and churches), and a love of hierarchy and discipline. Demagogues such as Hitler and Mussolini, he believes, have this type of personality structure. Adorno and his colleagues[74] largely agree with Allport's formulation but they also look back at the genesis of the condition and attribute it to 'a basically hierarchical, authoritarian, exploitive parent-child relationship'.

Animalisation

Anyone who lives in a Western culture is very well aware of the process of humanisation of animals (anthropomorphism). All sorts of people take a member of another species (usually cats, dogs, horses, etc) and endow the 'pet' with human quali-ties, projecting on to it all kinds of loving attributes that presumably they need or wish for. A pet like this can be particularly useful for lonely people whose supply of human affection is limited, or for individuals who find interacting with other humans a specially difficult task.

The reverse process can also occur, however, and it is quite possible for us to endow people with the qualities of other species (or at least with the qualities we assume to belong to other species). Very little study has been made of this psychological phenomenon and yet, as Tiger points out,[2] it may be of special importance in understanding human violence. If we can psychologically downgrade another person to a species we would normally kill or disregard it is clearly going to be easy for us to attack them. Presumably, if we designate a group as 'vermin' or the police as 'pigs', then they become an extreme type of out-group. They do not even belong to the same species, and inhibitions we may have about attacking our own kind are suspended. It is interesting that during World War I the British government issued pictures of German soldiers caricatured as pigs, no doubt an attempt to help the soldier overcome his natural repugnance for killing another man.

Such observations cast doubt on the purity of the distinction many zoologists make between intra-species violent behaviour and inter-species hunting behaviour. As we have seen, one can exist without the other—there are even different areas of the brain (in the cat) dealing with each behaviour—and it is nonsense to attribute man's violence largely to his carnivorous diet. Animalisation gives us, however, a process whereby we can call up our hunting skills and drive for use in another field of endeavour. Animalisation may well be unique to man.

'Criminals', an emotive term anyway, are frequently regarded as subhuman, as animals of one sort or another—'vermin', 'rats', 'They're not human' are all expressions used in connection with prisoners. Perhaps the ultimate in this process is exemplified by suggestions that no further operations should be carried out on live animals, but they should be performed instead on the inmates of Broadmoor—a hospital for insane and seriously disturbed criminals. Here we have anthropomorphism and animalisation acting simultaneously.

Learning

Human development is always dependent upon the nurture and education provided by the experienced adults in any given society, especially by the parents or substitute parents. We have already seen (p30) that if no adults of this kind are provided for rhesus monkeys, those monkeys are quite incapable of coping with an adult situation—in fact, they are fearful and aggressive. No human baby ever has to cope with an environmental disturbance as massive as that, but there is a great deal of evidence to suggest that babies born into deprived situations where they are handled cruelly or in a variety of ways conflicting with one another, or where they are starved of adult affection, also develop 'neurotic' problems as adults. In particular they find it difficult to get on well with other people and to adapt to the conflicting and strenuous demands made by adult life. In Chapter 7 we shall briefly consider the psychopath, an unruly undisciplined individual especially liable to break out into violence when under stress. He is almost always a product of one or more of the environmental misfortunes just outlined.

Our complicated social structure requires very powerful bond-making mechanisms. We depend utterly in our first years on other people, so we need to be attracted to them; but as we grow, this love, affection, or friendship must be a two-way process—we must give it as well as take it and at all times we must take into account the needs of others. This is a highly developed skill. If the school for love in our early years is a poor one, teaching us incorrect methods or perhaps no methods at all, we shall be deficient in this skill. We shall not consider other people sensitively: we shall put our own needs first in the short term, even if this is deleterious to our best interests in the long term, and we shall not know how to fit into a social hierarchy, nor how to abide by the rules of that hierarchy so as to advance ourselves within it. In all, we shall be subjected to an immense amount of frustration.

In the National Survey of Health and Development carried

out in Britain, in which 5,362 babies all born during one week in 1946 were followed until the age of 23, Douglas found the risks of delinquency to be higher than expected when a family had been broken by divorce or separation.[75] This finding has been repeated in different places and at different times throughout the world, and Nye[76] has indicated that the factors that lead to the broken home also lead to the delinquency, rather than the break itself leading to the delinquency. Hilda Lewis examined 500 deprived children[77] and found that 109 of them were particularly aggressive in their behaviour. She discovered that the aggressiveness was associated with a lack of affection for the father, illegitimacy, separation from the mother before the age of five, being in the care of an institution at a early age, and parental rejection. When a three-generation study was carried out in the late 1950s, less than 25 per cent of the children attending a child guidance clinic could boast two generations of unbroken homes.[78]

Looked at in slightly more subtle detail, a report published in 1957 of how 379 American mothers brought up their children from birth to kindergarten age[79] suggested that parents who love and accept their children, and use withdrawal of approval as a technique of discipline (rather than bribery or physical punishment), are most likely to produce children with a conscience; whereas inconsistent primitive methods of parental discipline, especially those involving aggressive methods of punishment, are more likely to produce an aggressive youngster. The peaceful home is characterised as one where the mother believes aggression is undesirable and discourages its expression by example and evident disapproval of it. In contrast, the home of angry outbursts is one that is tolerant or careless of aggression, or severely punitive, or both. As the authors of the report suggest, the way for parents to produce a non-aggressive child is to make it abundantly clear that aggression is frowned upon, and to stop aggression when it occurs, but to avoid punishing the child for his aggression. Punishment, while it stops a particular form of aggression, appears to generate more hostility in the child, and can lead to further aggressive outbursts at some other time or place. Furthermore, when parents punish, they are providing a living example of the use of aggression at the very moment they are trying to teach the child not to be aggressive. This last comment is specially important because it acknowledges the importance of 'imitative learning', which, as any parent knows, is a very powerful human educational process.[80]

Many criminologists are convinced that the cruel violent adult has learnt his unpleasant characteristics from his parents. A study of murderers reported in the *Journal of the American Medical Association* lends anecdotal support to this idea.[81] Six prisoners who had been convicted of first-degree murder were examined. They were middle-class whites who were not alcoholics, suffering from brain damage, or gang members. Four of them had suffered remorseless physical brutality in their own childhoods from their parents: one of the murderers, for instance, had been punished as a little boy by being held up by his feet while naked, beaten with a strap, and then dropped to the floor on to his head.

All this suggests that a child may learn violence from important parental figures. The quotation from Hibbert[11] given on p19 implied that if people are surrounded by violence and brutality, you can expect them to behave in a similar way. Is there then any experimental evidence that watching violence produces violent feelings or behaviour in the spectators? We shall see in Chapter 6 that a report on soccer violence in Britain firmly states that violence on the field produces violence on the terraces,[82] and anybody who has seen the audience drive away from the car park after watching a James Bond film or Grand Prix motor racing may well get the same impression. There is an alternative view, however, that watching violence is cathartic, that is it releases any pent-up feelings of aggression in a vicarious or secondhand way. Some go so far as to suggest that we should actually increase the amount of public violence to be witnessed so as to reduce the general level of pent-up aggressiveness in the community. Clearly this is a very important issue if we are serious in our attempts to curb violence, because this generation has one of the most powerful educational instruments ever invented in television, planted in the living-rooms of millions of homes.

Bandura, Ross and Ross have conducted a series of experiments to determine whether children imitate the violence they see. In one series[83] three groups of four-year-olds were set to watch an apparent TV show in which a man was playing with some toys and another man came in and tried to take them away. One group saw the intruder win and the defeated owner of the toys retire to a corner. Another group saw the owner beat up the intruder and the third (control) group saw the two men vigorously playing with the toys without attacking each other at all. Following these sequences the children were given some toys to play with, and just as they were getting interested in them they were taken away (ie, they were frustrated), and then they were allowed to play with toys like the ones they had seen on the TV. Those who watched the intruder win were more aggressive towards the toys than those who saw him lose. In the control group only the boys showed increased aggression, but here there was significantly less aggression than in the other two groups. Albert[84] took 220 children aged 8-10 years and divided them into three groups according to their scores of aggression on a projective test. They were then shuffled into three matched groups and shown a Western film. One group saw a conventional story with the hero winning, another saw the villain win, and the third group were left in the air with no resolution to the story. After the film shows each child had his aggression score taken again. The results were somewhat conflicting, although in all three situations about half of the initially high aggression scorers had their scores reduced. However, between one-third and one-half of the children watching the conventional Western had their scores increased.

It is quite possible, indeed probable, that any kind of

aggressive example set by adults or peers will be followed with similar behaviour by a child, but television is of special importance, because once it is widely introduced into a community the operators of the TV networks have the power to influence large numbers of people at the same time. They probably do not have any more influence than, say, a schoolteacher, but any one teacher only influences twenty to forty children at a time, and a TV programme may be seen by millions and so could introduce conformity. Nevertheless many of us believe that behaviour is only likely to be affected marginally by TV programmes because personality structure, which is a prime factor in behaviour, only changes by interpersonal interaction and even then not very rapidly. Furthermore, any effects are likely to be overwhelmed by more potent influences, such as work, family life, etc.

In 1958 a British report was published called *Television and the Child*.[85] It was found at that time (when network time and channel choice were strictly limited) that British children who could watch TV did so for 11-13 hours per week, and their favourite programmes were thrillers and Westerns. The authors thought that viewing had a broadening effect on the child, making him more ambitious but also more tolerant of other people. On the whole the children were not disturbed by the violence they saw and fiction seemed to make a bigger impact than newsreel material. Guns were regarded as less frightening than daggers. Children were, however, disturbed by situations in which they could identify themselves. The authors could find no evidence that viewers were more aggressive in behaviour than non-viewers, although they warned that TV violence could precipitate violence in the disturbed child. On the other hand, there was no evidence that violent TV programmes were beneficial; they could arouse aggression as easily as they could discharge it. In view of their findings the authors recommended a reduction in the number of programmes of crime and violence shown at peak children's hours. In an American survey published in 1961 Schramm and his colleagues[86] found many similar features, and also warned that vulnerable children could confuse fantasy with reality and transfer violence from the screen into the real world. They quoted one or two 'near misses', where children imitated violence they had seen on TV—like the 17 year old youths who went sniping with a pistol from a car after watching a programme depicting this activity. In a review of the relevant literature Hartley[87] is very critical of the viewpoint taken by the imitative theorists like Bandura and Walters. She complains that individual differences have been ignored and stresses that people are capable of encapsulating a phantasy TV world and separating it from reality, which is so different.

Training
When we looked at how Scott and other zoologists trained mice to be better fighters (p32), we noticed that they gave the mice to be trained an easy start and rewarded them for success in fighting. In this way they became more and more proficient in battles. Something very akin to this occurs in humans when they teach one another to fight—boxing, wrestling, judo, weaponry, military tactics, flying a fighter aircraft, etc. The subject concerned is taught to use his violence equipment, whatever it may be, to the best advantage possible, and it is possible that the outcome of a war could depend upon the proficiency of violence training for each of the contesting armies.

Clearly the training of men to be good fighters does not of itself cause a violent outburst (although a well-trained army may exacerbate the paranoid fears of a potential enemy). However, the quality and extent of training given to an individual or a group of individuals will undoubtedly colour the nature of any ensuing combat and may determine its outcome. Maybe man's enormous capacity for learning skills is one reason why he is such a deadly fighter. He uses every device and technique he can muster and often is trained to use them very well.

During the late 1930s the Nazis applied these principles to an extreme degree. They took young men and by a process of stern and vicious training, which included a great deal of physical violence against the trainees, systematically turned out a large number of specialists in violence. This process we may now call 'brutalisation' but it certainly produced tough effective SS men and members of the Gestapo who were prepared to kill, to torture, and who seemed expert and uninhibited in these tasks.

Cooperativeness and Obedience

I have already emphasised that one of the important characteristics of a social animal is its cooperativeness. Living in groups brings advantages, but to live in a group necessitates cooperation and deference to the needs of the group. Sometimes group needs and individual needs come into conflict and a happy balance has to be struck between priority for one and priority for the other. This means that on occasions group needs must take precedence over individual needs. Man is a highly developed social animal and his cooperativeness has reached a level not achieved by any other mammal. In almost every essential biological activity—feeding, collecting food, building homes, coping with the elements, defence against predators, etc—man cooperates with man. It could well be argued that this high degree of mutual cooperation is one of the key factors in man's successful evolution. Certainly man has utilised one of the major advantages of group living— division of labour—to a much greater extent than any other mammal. Because we cooperate in groups we can each develop our own special skill and devote most of our time to that, relying on the labour of others for the rest of our requirements. Most of us in Western society spend very little time in producing, gathering or even preparing our daily food. We rely almost exclusively on the skills of others for these essentials.

If a group is, for some psychological, territorial or other reason, in direct competition with another group, each group will try to defend itself against the other. In that group defence cooperativeness will be very prominent and important. We saw this in the battle between rhesus monkeys in India (p41). Obviously when war breaks out between one human group and another, cooperativeness and division of labour are crucial. The technology of war (even primitive war) demands specialised skills (being an archer or a gunner, for example). Weapons demand supplies and, therefore, a complicated organisation to get them to the battle-front. It is probably significant that the only other creatures that have developed anything resembling human warfare are the social insects[25] and they, too, are highly cooperative, with a marked division of labour. One facet of cooperation is of special importance. As we have seen from the animal studies, an ordered society requires leadership, it requires a hierarchy, it requires dominance and submission, and it requires deference to the group needs. All this adds up to 'obedience'. When a group decision has been taken, it is imperative for the continuation of that group that all members comply with the decision.

Man is a very obedient creature. This, too, may have some connection with his successful evolution. We can all think of occasions when men are not obedient, but these are newsworthy exceptions and even then, if we inquire into the situation at all closely, we often find that what we are really seeing is an inter-group clash, with one group refusing to obey one leader but willingly accepting the authority of another. An industrial strike illustrates this point quite well. It does not follow (as is sometimes thought) that removal of a leader necessarily destroys a group's cohesion, because groups can usually throw up successive leaders whom they will obey assiduously. If the reader has any doubts about the obedience of a group of men, let him look at some film of the pre-war European dictators, or go to a Billy Graham religious rally or an orchestral concert to see how thousands of people can be roused, or stilled almost instantly, at the whim of a respected leader.

The use of obedience and its value to mankind can be seen in the space programme. Thousands of individuals need to cooperate in the most complex way, and for much of the time most of them are taking instructions from others higher up the hierarchy. The ultimate illustration of the power of obedience is the space flight itself. Here we have two or three men, sometimes thousands of miles from the Earth in a hostile environment, taking, almost without question, complex orders from the space base and from computers. This powerful facility of man to obey instructions is of immense survival value. Just stop to think for one moment, however, of a large group of brutalised men in a well knit hierarchy given an instruction to be violent. Result, the Gestapo or its equivalent.

In war obedience is vital. Clearly, not every soldier feels hostile to every enemy soldier all the time. Sometimes he may wonder what the war is about anyway. This is clearly illustrated by another reference to World War I. During one of the agreed Christmas truces German and British soldiers came out of their trenches, shook hands, and swapped mementoes. Not the behaviour of deadly enemies you might think, and yet the next day they were killing one another as usual. How did this happen? Quite simply, they were ordered to fight and in spite of the absence of hostile feelings they obeyed. It could be argued that they only obeyed from fear. This is unlikely but, whatever the reason, they obeyed. A military hierarchy (like any other hierarchy) depends upon obedience, and functions because of it.

Most of us would like to think that we are not going to be that obedient in violence, that we could certainly not carry out orders to shoot somebody just because somebody above us in a hierarchy told us to do so. We hope we would think for ourselves, and would refuse to run a concentration camp where people starve to death, just because it was the job that we had been given. Are our hopes well founded? True enough, some of us would resist such orders, perhaps even if it meant our own death, but many of us would not, as repeated wars and violent horrors have shown. The truth of this has been demonstrated in a laboratory experiment by Milgram.[88, 89] He took forty men aged 20-50 years from a wide range of occupations (postal clerks, labourers, engineers) by advertising for some volunteers to participate in a learning experiment. The subjects were told that they had to train another subject who was in the next room by giving him an electric shock whenever he made an incorrect response to a problem. The equipment included a handle with which he could increase the voltage of the shock administered, at 300v the dial was marked 'painful', at 420v it was marked 'danger severe shock' and the dial ended at 450v. When the subject who was learning made repeated errors the volunteer was instructed by the experimenter to increase the strength of the punishing shock. Twenty-six men (62 per cent) went right to the maximum reading on the dial, that is, 450v or two points past the danger notice! In fact, the recipient of the shocks was an accomplice of the experimenter and the current did not actually reach him, but Milgram is convinced that the volunteers were unaware of this, partly because of the realism of the experiment, partly because of the distress shown by the volunteers as they administered the shocks, and partly because they all said later they thought the situation was real. At 315v the victim pounded on the wall and then stopped responding to the learning situation. The experimenter told the volunteer to regard the lack of response as an error and to punish it with bigger shocks. 'You have no choice, you must go on,' he would say. All the volunteers went up to 300v (marked painful), 35 to 315v, 31 to 330v, 29 to 345v, 28 to 360v, 27 to 375v, and 26 to 450v.

As Milgram notes: 'With numbing regularity good people were seen to knuckle under the demands of authority and to perform actions that were callous and severe. Men who, in everyday life, are responsible and decent were seduced by the trappings of authority.'

References to this chapter appear on pp184-5

5 *Social Factors and Individual Violence*

Much of the discussion in Chapters 3 and 4 has tended to imply that there is a creature we can label 'a violent man', or at least there is a human continuum with extremely violent people and extremely non-violent people at either end. The violent men in this scheme of things are seen as having a different physiology and a different psychology from their non-violent compatriots. For some purposes this is an entirely acceptable approach (see also p145), but it takes no account of the environmental stresses and pressures to which we are all constantly subjected. Previously I have also tried to emphasise the importance of man as a social animal living in groups, and that environmental stimuli such as frustrations often act as a trigger for violence. It is time for us to consider some of these external environmental factors.

Overcrowding
We have already seen that changes in social pressures and interactions will produce changes in other primates—even violence can be induced—and so it should not surprise us if we find similar factors operating in human societies. Desmond Morris[90] has tried to convince us that civilisation has produced

a kind of artificial zoo and, therefore, that we, too, are subject to all the ills of living in an artificial confined space. The Russells[25] have set out in their book the thesis that 'the problem of violence is fundamentally the problem of population; if we can solve the one we can solve the other'. Overcrowding, it seems, has become our contemporary *bête noire*, responsible for all our ills. As many writers have indicated, it is indeed vital for a whole variety of reasons to control the growth of our population, and it is possible that violence is related somewhat to overcrowding (after all, violent crime is largely confined to cities and riots rarely occur in rural areas), but the Russells' view is too simplistic. Carstairs[91] also supports the overcrowding theory, but he brings in the concepts of alienation and despair, which are not necessarily directly related to overcrowding, and concludes: 'Unless the masses of our city poor can be persuaded that there is a future for them too in the Great Society, their morale is likely to crumble until vast human communities degenerate into the semblance of concentration camp inmates, if not to that of Zuckerman's pathologically belligerent apes'. Despair, alienation, and thwarted aspiration can all be seen as related to frustration, and we should examine them separately.

One of the disconcerting features of wartime concentration camps was the fact that very little violence took place among the overcrowded prisoners, and they did not riot or attack their guards. This was at least partly related to starvation (see p34) but even when prisoners in all sorts of situations are well fed, riots and serious violence are newsworthy, not commonplace. Also, as we have seen, the violence that occurred amongst Zuckerman's monkeys could be attributed to other factors besides overcrowding: the inhabitants of Monkey Hill were not brought up together, and there was a disturbed sex ratio. Moreover it is interesting that war does not seem to be especially related to overcrowding. Richardson[92] in his mammoth statistical analysis of war concludes that the increase in world population from 1820-1949 does not seem to have been accompanied by a proportionate increase in the frequency of, and loss of life from, war; in fact there is a suggestion that mankind has become less warlike since 1820. A densely populated part of the world—China—has contributed very little to the war statistics. Nearer home, Scandinavia is a very good example of increasing population not being correlated with an increase in violence.

Nevertheless, on a purely statistical level, if more and more people are pressed into a fixed space, they will meet one another more often, interact more often, and the probability of quarrels will be increased. Equally, if we are confronted with hundreds of thousands of direct competitors instead of just one or two, the chances of being frustrated go up accordingly.

All animal species have to control their populations, and we are no exception. Usually this is done by balancing the birthrate with the deathrate of any given group. If imbalance occurs, some other factors will have to operate. For some centuries now man has been in imbalance, his birthrate exceeding his deathrate. In the last 100 years or so this imbalance has been increased by medical care and the conquest of the infectious diseases. So far this problem has been dealt with by two mechanisms—catastrophes, when populations have fallen sharply, and colonisation of previously uninhabited land. We have now almost run out of new areas of land unless the moon is to prove our new salvation, so we must either rely upon catastrophes or birth control. As Cipolla[93] has pointed out, most of the previous catastrophes of mankind have been famines or plagues (the Black Death, smallpox, cholera and the like), but a few have been devastating wars.

While accepting, then, that population control is essential to prevent catastrophes, and that violence tends to occur in crowded situations, we shall have to look deeper than overcrowding alone to find the social factors relating to violence. In Chapter 4 considerable emphasis was given to frustration as a cause of aggression and it seems reasonable, therefore, to look for causes of social frustration.

Social Frustration

Right back in 1925 a British study[94] showed a relation between the business cycle (computed from government statistics about unemployment, exports, retail prices, coal production, etc) from 1904 to 1913 and the reported statistics for crime. Drunkenness went up during phases of prosperity, while thieving increased during depressions. The poor years also had higher figures for completed suicides. A much later study[95] looked at the same phenomenon in the United States. Burglary, robbery, suicide and lynching of negroes all increased during the years of depression, and homicide seemed to go up during prosperity. As we shall see in Chapter 8, it is probably unsafe to put too much weight on fluctuations in official statistics, but for what they are worth these investigations suggest a relation between the frustrations of economic recession and some forms of crime—perhaps even violent crime.

One of the better known and more widely accepted theories of social frustration was put forward by R. K. Merton in the 1930s. He suggested[96] that we must examine in any given situation two important social factors: (1) the culturally defined goals, purposes and interests, and (2) the acceptable modes of achieving these goals. In other words, he accepts man as a striving aggressive creature and believes that important factors in determining behaviour are the culture he finds himself in, what he is aiming to achieve, and how he can set out to achieve those aims. The goals he postulates are set by the culture, and may be skills in hunting, in acquiring money, in sexual prowess, in asceticism, etc. Some modes or means of achievement are acceptable to the society but others are not. For example, if money is a social goal, achievement by adhering to stock-market rules or recognised company practice is acceptable, even laudable, but achievement by fraud, however clever in its planning and execution, is unacceptable. Merton defines five logically possible types of response to the situation we all find ourselves in, which he illustrates in the following way:

		Culture goals	Means
I	Conformity	+	+
II	Innovation	+	−
III	Ritualism	−	+
IV	Retreatism	−	−
V	Rebellion	±	±

In the diagram + signifies acceptance, − signifies elimination, and ± signifies rejection and substitution of new goals and standards. Merton believes that Solution I, Conformity to both goals and means, is the commonest, while IV, Retreatism, by rejecting all society's values—alienation, as shown by some tramps and dropouts—is the least common. Solution II is of course the delinquent's answer: society's goals—money and possessions, for example—seem worthwhile having but they are unattainable via acceptable means, either because the goals set are unrealistic (not everybody can be rich) or because of personal problems, and the result is frustration and innovation, ie, delinquency, perhaps stealing or robbery. He cites Al Capone as 'the triumph of amoral intelligence over morally prescribed "failure" when the channels of vertical mobility are closed or narrowed in a society which places a high premium on economic affluence and social ascent for *all* its members'.

The attraction of Merton's theory is that in some measure it has been predictive, because it suggests that if a society sets its goals at more and more unrealistic levels, more and more members will experience frustration and turn to innovation. Maybe this is the present-day situation, where we have efficient communication systems telling us all we must be 'successful' and defining success in terms of status property—houses, motor cars, television sets and the like—and status sex. Furthermore, it suggests that increasing affluence in a society is not necessarily associated with a diminishing crime rate. If there is more property available, then the competition for it will intensify, the accepted means will become difficult and so we shall end up with an increasingly large number of individuals who accept the goals but cannot employ the accepted means. If everybody is taught that it is desirable to make a fortune, many will be frustrated, and some will take short cuts, such as fraud, theft, robbery and the like.

Anomie

Much of Merton's thinking was a development of the views of Emile Durkheim, an eminent French sociologist of the nineteenth century who postulated the notion of anomie—a kind of normlessness or deregulation in which social constraints were loosened. It seemed to him that in earlier societies every individual knew his defined limits—'the rich man in his castle, the poor man at his gate'—and expected no movement outside those limits. As societies have changed, however, there is more possibility of social movement; in fact, many of us now subscribe to the idea of equality of opportunity. In its extreme form this suggests that every American child has the opportunity to become President. Durkheim suggested that this feeling of enormous opportunity, together with the realities of limited mechanisms, was related to one form of violent death —suicide.[97]

Durkheim[98] was also responsible for first suggesting that crime is completely normal. Others[99] have gone further and suggested that it is usual rather than criminal behaviour that needs an explanation. Durkheim suggested that every society, even the most saintly, will always define some aspect of behaviour as deviant, and will, therefore, be able to point the finger of scorn at a transgressor. He also suggests that the type of crime found commonly in a society is a reflection of the average type of conscience in that society. In a monastery with high standards strictly adhered to gluttony or talking during periods of silence will be regarded as severe offences. Conversely, if murder, robbery, and bloodshed are commonplace in a society, it will be found that violence is to some degree acceptable to that society, or, in Durkheim's words: 'For murder to disappear, the horror of bloodshed must become greater in those social strata from which murderers are recruited; but, first, it must become greater throughout the entire society.' In other words, it is sometimes easier and more pertinent to talk of a violent society than of violent individuals.

Subculture Theories

In some measure all these authors are suggesting that in any society we should expect 'subcultures' where criminal traditions and skills are fairly widespread. The truth of this supposition is partly exemplified by police work, which concentrates upon the 'underworld' and known criminal areas in large towns. Quite a lot of study has been made of 'criminal areas' and there seems no doubt at all that some areas of a nation or of a town produce more evident crime than others. In Britain, for example, armed robbery is an almost entirely urban occurrence and is largely confined to the South-east of England, especially the London area, although quite recently it has spread to other huge conurbations. In their classic study of Chicago, Shaw and McKay[100] showed that the older, more run-down areas of the city had an especially high proportion of delinquents. Many other studies[101] have also indicated that particular areas—often underprivileged—are specially associated with criminal activities. As far as violence is concerned, several recent examples stand out prominently—the ghetto riots of black America in 1967, Londonderry and Belfast in Northern Ireland in the 1970s. A BBC television programme ('Cities at Breaking Point'—28 November 1970) examined the Dingle area of Liverpool in Britain. Vandalism is rife, the television reporters had their car attacked and the radio ripped out whilst it was left unattended. After surveying the area, however, they were not surprised, for it is all being destroyed by the city authorities to make way for new housing. This process has been going on for some years and many of the children have seen property destroyed day after day for the whole of their lives. They are never quite certain where they will move to or when. They see other people with better possessions and more stability and they become resentful and aggressive; and their daily experience teaches them that property is for destruction.

It is relevant at this stage to consider the prison subculture that society manufactures. The eminent Italian criminologist Cesare Lombroso called prisons the 'universities of crime', by which he meant that most criminals received their further education in the skills of crime within the prison walls. This is probably still true today. Consider our action with the convicted criminal, especially the younger lad. By the court process he is labelled as bad and is sentenced to be temporarily outlawed within a prison where he will meet hundreds of similarly placed men. This process makes it clear to him that he (not just his behaviour but he himself) is unacceptable to society. Frequently this will lead to a feeling of rejection and resentment, and it will certainly emphasise that the tantalising cultural goals are well out of reach. Thrown together in this way, prisoners who may be markedly dissimilar in many ways find much in common through their circumstances and, inevitably, try to form a subculture of their own. Fortunately they are not very successful at this, for many of them have difficulties with personal relationships that inhibit the process. Even so, sufficient cohesion is formed for the less emotionally crippled to swap ideas, to teach one another criminal skills, to put one another in touch with important sources of information or equipment, and to strike up new groupings that may be of value when they continue their illegitimate struggle towards the goals set by society, on their release. In a recent study I made of long-term prisoners there were twenty-eight robbers, all but two of whom had served in penal institutions before taking to robbery, and many of whom admitted that they learned the know-how or joined with other men to carry out the robberies because of previous prison experience. Two clear exceptions were a coloured immigrant from an American ghetto, and a young Scot reared in Glasgow's gang land. The best exponent of the subculture theory as far as violence is concerned is Marvin Wolfgang.[102] He postulates that violence is largely confined to a relatively homogeneous subcultural group, where it is one of the accepted norms. The group's members are taught that the way to achieve success or riches is to fight for it, not in the subtle non-violent way that is often meant by this phraseology, but with fists, weapons and real violence. Wolfgang came to his conclusions after a study of American murderers. He has decided that the violent subculture exists among underprivileged males of the lower social groups, especially among underprivileged negro males in the American ghettos. Certainly there is evidence that some American lower-class boys see themselves as tough, more fearless, powerful and dangerous more often than do middle-class boys,[103] but it is not at all clear that violence in all its various guises is related to lower social class in quite this way. The advantage of Wolfgang's theory is that it stops us thinking of all violent criminals as in some way 'mental', and reminds us that it is possible for some groups of people to be taught that violence is the correct and proper solution to difficult problems.

Victims

We shall consider crimes in more detail in Chapter 8, but here it is pertinent to emphasise that if we are talking about violence between people, let us say a fight between two men, then there is more than one individual involved. Pretty obvious, I dare say, but it is not quite as simple as the victim–offender arrangement that we often think of. It is possible for an innocent bystander to be attacked by a deranged or mistaken aggressor but this is exceedingly unlikely and must be very rare. Nearly always the violence is directed at a particular person or a particular group. Usually there is a good deal of contact between two contestants before a fight breaks out, and during the fight the behaviour of one influences the other. There may well be a great deal of provocation.

A book published recently from California[104] focused on

violent incidents between 'criminals' and police. Vivid descriptions are given of how trivial incidents escalate into terrifying battles, but even more significantly it indicates that some policemen are particularly likely to be assaulted, and that this is understandable when their behaviour is analysed. For a variety of reasons, usually quite unconscious, they actually aggravate a difficult situation rather than calm it.

Social Mores

Different cultures have different social mores and different levels of violence. One interesting aspect we in the English-speaking world should examine is the difference in existing social conditions on the two sides of the Atlantic, for Britain and the United States have differing rates of violence. Alas, this is all too difficult because the data about the social structures of these two countries is not neatly assembled or readily available. We can only make theories and informed guesses, just scratch the surface in fact. In Chapter 6 we shall examine the American problem of the ghetto riots. Here two differences between the countries are worth briefly mentioning—their histories and their attitudes to weapons.

Roberts[10] has endorsed Asa Briggs' description of Britain between 1783 and 1867 as 'the age of improvement' and pointed out that during this period the country changed from a conflict-ridden society in which mob violence was matched by the savage brutality of hangings and transportation for life to a society in which conflict was resolved much more peaceably. He suggests that the main factors in bringing about this transformation were economic growth, political reform, moral suasion and institutional developments. America, on the other hand, had to force its way on to the international stage with a war of independence. Brown[105] points out that throughout its short history there has been a huge amount of violence in the United States, much of it associated with glory and the construction of a 'better' America—the War of Independence itself, the freeing of the slaves and the preservation of the

Union in the Civil War, the takeover of the land from the Indians, and the stabilisation of frontier society by vigilante violence. In fact, violence is traditional; 'the patriot, the humanitarian, the nationalist, the pioneer, the landholder, the farmer, and the laborer' have all used violence to achieve their objectives in the fairly recent past. 'So great has been our involvement with both negative and positive violence over the long sweep of our history that violence has truly become a part of our unacknowledged (or underground) value structure.' [105]

It is a lack of understanding of this history that makes some of us non-Americans gasp at the United States gun-law problem. Violence by firearm comes to the world's attention with the assassination of a President or a Presidential candidate, and such violence is one of the curses of modern America, rooted in its emotional history. As we have seen in an earlier chapter, a lethal weapon transforms a heated momentary or not too serious conflict into a macabre tragedy. In the United States guns are freely available, indeed regarded by many as one component of 'freedom'—there is a National Rifle Association with over 1 million members and an annual budget of over \$5 million[106] which successfully lobbies the government of America not to bring in regulatory controls against weapons. In 1967 someone was shot to death, somewhere in the United States, once every 25 minutes, guns were involved in the deaths of 21,000 civilians (7,700 homicides, 11,000 suicides and 2,800 accidents), and guns were also used in 71,000 armed robberies and 55,000 assaults. That year about 63 per cent of all homicides and 50 per cent of all suicides were shootings.[107] It would, of course, be naive to attribute all the wide difference in homicide rates between Britain and America to the differing social attitudes to guns, but perhaps we should not be amazed that a society that dislikes guns so much that it will not even allow policemen to carry them has a very low homicide rate with only 0.6 deaths/100,000 population (murders, suicides and accidents) from firearms compared with 11.1/

100,000 in the USA. Recently in London armed men took part in a bank raid. They were prepared to use their arms and shot a member of the bank staff in the hand. A single unarmed policeman ran up at the crucial moment, but all he could do was to protect a baby from being harmed, and the robbers got away with the money. When he was questioned about the incident on television that evening, he complained that he was only armed with 'a bit of wood'—his truncheon. I can only hope his colleagues later pointed out to him that if the robbers had not been certain that he was unarmed, they would almost certainly have shot him and a few other people, too.

References to this chapter appear on pp185-6

6 *Group Violence*

So far we have concentrated upon violence in individuals, and, of course, ultimately all violence is concerned with individuals; but it should never be forgotten that the really serious forms of human violence are group phenomena, war being the ultimate. We have already seen (p69) that man's dominant position in terrestrial evolution is dependent upon the combination of his intensely gregarious and his intensely aggressive natures. The power to destroy the world and all its inhabitants is the ultimate expression of this dominance.

Group Mechanisms

All too little is known about the kinds of group that man operates in and the group mechanisms he uses, but it is fairly obvious that for health and comfort each of us needs a group to belong to—a family, a circle of friends, a club, a union, a firm, a nation, a race and so forth. Belonging to any particular group is more than just being labelled as such, it carries emotional and psychological aspects such as commitment to the group. In Chapter 7 we shall consider people who find it impossible to form these emotional and psychological ties, and they are usually extremely uncomfortable and at a great disadvantage.

Equally obviously, human groups have a hierarchical structure involving leaders and subordinates, a chain of command, and varying degrees of responsibility and privilege. Within the group there may well be struggles for power and privilege, and sub-groupings can take place. The clear implication of belonging to a group is that there are others who do not belong. Sumner[108] talked of the 'we-group or in-group' and its opposite the 'others-group or out-group', and he suggested that the very existence of the two groups produces conflict and a relationship of 'war and plunder, except so far as agreements have modified it'. This may be taking an extreme point of view but it seems logical that if we belong to a group for cooperation and self-advancement, because we cannot operate as successfully on our own, then those who do not belong to our group but to some other group may well be in competition with and so pose a threat to us. We have already briefly examined the psychology of feeling threatened and have seen that defensiveness and aggressiveness may result.

The powerful ability of individuals to join together into a cohesive in-group resisting competition from the out-group was shown by Blake and Mouton.[109] They demonstrated what they called 'the traitor trap'. Groups of seven to twelve people met for five or six two-hour sessions on three successive days and in that short time they formed cohesive groups. The experiment consisted of giving each group some 3 hours to prepare a solution in the form of a memo to a problem. The solutions were then swapped and considered by another group for a further 1-2 hours. Each group elected a spokesman who spent 2-4 hours in discussion and argument with the other spokesmen, and the object of the exercise was to get the representatives to agree on the best or winning solution. Out of the sixty-two representatives used in the experiment only two voted against their group's solution. The experimenters concluded that 'loyalty to an in-group position replaces the exercise of logic' when groups are in competition under these kinds of win–lose conditions.

In his recent book *Men in Groups* Tiger[2] has suggested that most of the important grouping behaviour in human society occurs between males, and that males have a special non-erotic bonding ability that throws them together to perform the masculine social functions such as defence, organisation of food supplies, and protection of females and young. He quotes example after example of all-male situations where loyalty to the group is of prime importance—secret societies, armies, political affiliations, sports clubs and so on. His view is that much of human group behaviour depends upon this male–male bond, which in turn is related to aggressiveness. Certainly males seem of special importance in large-scale group activities, and group violence is an almost exclusively male activity.

Clearly, then, the study of group violence is more than merely the study of individual violence in a larger form. The structure, the cooperativeness, the division of labour following from cooperativeness, and the hierarchical obedience that exists in a social group, are all important entities in their own right, adding an entirely new dimension to group behaviour. Some authors have gone so far as to postulate a 'collective mind' existing over and above the minds of the individuals in a group. However, as Sprott[110] points out, there is no need to theorise in such abstract terms, simpler explanations for the special phenomena of group behaviour sufficing. He suggests that the two most important of these are (1) heightened emotionality and (2) a lowered sense of responsibility. Heightened emotionality is simply a magnification of the feelings the individuals comprising the group are experiencing. All the feelings we considered in Chapter 4 can, of course, be heightened and the process is brought about by each individual being surrounded by other people sharing the same feeling. It is of biological advantage for fear, shall we say, to be spread rapidly through a threatened group, and so produce a mass response. Each individual sees fear on the face of all the surrounding individuals and his own fear is thereby triggered or heightened. During a battle leaders will deliberately raise emotions such as paranoia, which will produce a fighting response. By a lowered sense of responsibility Sprott means a diminution of the powers of criticism and a slackening of the normal internal controls that arises from the impression of universality, the notion that so many people cannot be wrong. In any group we are rewarded for conforming and penalised for eccentricity, and so if we are well integrated into a group, we tend to accept its beliefs whatever the logic behind them.

One characteristic sometimes imputed to a group or crowd is that the whole behaves in a much less seemly way than the individuals who comprise it would if they were alone—as if the crowd develops its own conscience, which is less stringent than any one individual's would be. Sprott refutes this idea and suggests that a crowd's behaviour depends upon its leadership—for any given situation one type of leadership will lead the group to violence, another perhaps to heroism—but he also admits that the prevailing social climate that the group finds itself in is also an important determinant of outcome. As we shall see below, riots and revolutions are usually found in a setting of tension.

Sanctioned and Unsanctioned Violence

Aggressiveness, with its ultimate threat of violence, and especially group violence, is probably of great survival value. It is possible that as mammalian society has evolved, violence, or the threat of violence, has been a factor in producing group cohesion. Hence the very real and cogent feeling that some forms of violence are justified, necessary, good. Even Jesus Christ, who preached a very powerfully pacific doctrine, is seen at one point in his life to have erupted into violence when he became angry at seeing the moneychangers in the Temple. His, of course, was not group violence and it was not widely sanctioned, but it illustrates that for most human doctrines there comes a point where violence is regarded as justified. Almost as a corollary, justifiable violence in the eyes of one group is unjustified in the eyes of another. In Chapter 5 we briefly looked at Wolfgang's 'subculture of violence' hypothesis in which he suggests that certain forms of violence, including criminal violence, which are forbidden by the ruling groups and perhaps the majority of people in western societies, are acceptable to a small sub-group of relatively underprivileged people in the same countries.

The problems raised by sanctioned and non-sanctioned violence have recently been illustrated by the trial of Lieutenant Calley in the United States for his part in the My Lai massacre, in which dozens of unarmed Vietnamese citizens, including women and children, were mercilessly shot. In legal terms he stepped over the boundaries laid down by the law, but it is clear in terms of the social mores that a large number of Americans regarded his violence as legitimate. In fact there is a current polarisation of view about the war in Vietnam which soldiers such as Calley have been caught in. One half of the nation group is saying the war is unjustified and are, therefore, repelled by the type of civilian slaughter that Calley was involved in; the other half accepts the North Vietnamese as enemies to be defeated at any price and have, therefore, given overt support to this kind of violence. This is a very complicated situation for any unsophisticated soldier, because to be a hero in the eyes of one half of the nation automatically makes one a 'criminal' in the eyes of the other half.

It is interesting to note the defence Calley used: he claimed that (a) he was acting under orders, (b) he was suffering from battle stress and (c) he did not regard the Vietnamese as human beings—classic illustrations of the mechanisms discussed earlier of obedience, fear and animalisation.

Violent Gangs

For very many years Thrasher's[111] views on the criminal gang were used as the basis of all discussion on the subject. He was writing, however, about the organised gangs of prewar Chicago and there are probably many different types of criminal gang—not all of them violent.

One of the best recent reviews of the literature relating to the criminal and the violent gang is to be found in Yablonsky's book[112] *The Violent Gang*. He quotes from Herbert Asbury's *Gangs of New York*, which makes it clear that at the turn of this century there were some fearful gangs in that city—the Bowery Boys, the Atlantic Guards and so on—many of them ruling their own territory with terror and violence, successfully keeping the police at bay. At one time gang violence was accepted in cities such as New York as one of the hazards of life, but now, according to Yablonsky, there is much more open condemnation of it and the police are to some extent supported in their work.

Yablonsky points out that the history of gang theories can be divided into two phases—the Chicago school, of which Thrasher is the best known exponent, 1920-1940, and the postwar 'theory builders'. Thrasher studied some 1,313 separate cases and noted that the gang boys came from dilapidated industrial areas and their delinquency was seen as a natural progression from a childhood search for excitement in a ghastly environment. As we have already seen, studies have confirmed that some parts of British cities also throw up more than their fair share of delinquents (see p79). Yablonsky summarises the Chicago School theory as gang development in eight stages: (1) a boy starts with malicious mischief, (2) this causes him to conflict with society, (3) he joins a gang, (4) the gang becomes a cohesive entity, (5) the gang conflicts with society, (6) the gang becomes a school for crime, (7) properly organised crime follows, and (8) the youth moves up the delinquency hierarchy. Other theories have now overshadowed Thrasher's work, but this type of escalation theory still seems to be fundamental to the understanding of some criminal activities.

For Yablonsky's second phase of 'theory builders' we have to return to the theories of Merton, which we looked at in Chapter 5. Extensions of Merton's theory have been made by workers such as Cohen[113] and Cloward and Ohlin.[114] In Cohen's view the gang serves as a focus of 'attraction, loyalty and solidarity' for youths who otherwise find themselves without the means to achieve the goals set by society. In the gang boys can achieve status by reversing the values of the rest of society—by delinquency and by violence. Cloward and Ohlin see crime as primarily aimed at gaining wealth, with the criminal accepting the financial goals of society.

Mays[115] drew attention to the possibility of delinquent subcultures also existing in the UK. He interviewed some eighty youth-club members in Liverpool and concluded that delinquency was the norm, thirty of the eighty having appeared before the courts and many of the others admitting to undetected delinquency. Mays regarded the delinquencies as an 'adjustment to a subculture in conflict with the culture of the city as a whole'. As he explained later,[116] 'It seemed to me that excessive leisure time, the absence of adequate parental models and care, the presence of known adult offenders in the locality together with the boys' own natural desire to test themselves in acts of daring, bravado, and danger, were a sufficient explanation for delinquent behaviour which invariably tapered off after leaving school and was almost certainly phasic in character'.

Yablonsky has attempted his own classification of gangs and grades them into three categories. Type I is the social gang, a relatively permanent organisation that centres around a specific location such as a shop or a clubhouse. Members know one another, they often wear a badge or insignia, and leadership is informal and based upon popularity. This type of gang rarely participates in delinquent behaviour or gang warfare and on the whole acts in terms of the values of the larger society. Yablonsky's Type II is the delinquent gang that is primarily organised to carry out various illegal acts. Membership is not easily achieved and the leader is the most effective thief and best planner of crimes. Most of the members are emotionally stable youths. Violence may be employed as a means towards the end of acquiring material and financial rewards. The

'violent gang' is Type III in Yablonsky's system, and he believes it to be primarily organised for emotional gratification.
Violence is the theme around which all activities centre. Small
arsenals of weapons are accumulated. Leadership is characterised by megalomania, and the leader is glorified by gang
members to enhance their own self-concept. Pseudo-territorial
disputes are a constant source of inter-gang conflict.

In 1953 Professor Yablonsky was appointed to direct a crime
prevention programme on the upper West Side of Manhattan
and for four years he lived and worked in the area, mixing
with the gangs and delinquents. Inevitably, therefore, his
views are somewhat local to New York, but they generate
useful concepts for the problem of violent gangs in general.
In New York violent gangs appear to emerge spontaneously,
and joining up is a relatively easy process, as indeed is 'quit-
ting', which can be voluntary or at the whim of the leader.
The leaders are self-appointed, often beginning and organis-
ing the gang, and they frequently have ideas of persecution or
grandeur in which they talk of controlling vast networks of
gang alliances. 'Their wild dreams of glory often serve their
pathological needs and those of the gang.' Gang wars can
easily be precipitated by seemingly trivial incidents involving
territory, a 'bad look', an exaggerated argument over a girl, or
a nasty remark. Looking for a reason for gang development,
Yablonsky sees it as arising from a blend of negative physical
and social forces—the slums, the overcrowding, the underlying
human decay and barrenness. 'The violent gang emerging
from this type of asocial community forms a bizarre replica of
the "community" that spawned it.'

When Dr Peter Scott[117] looked at London, he found there
were almost no coherent gangs at all; 86 per cent of boys who
committed crimes in a group situation and were sent to a
remand home were from loose unstructured associations, only
seventeen boys out of 151 belonged to proper gangs, and violence seemed not to be prominent. In more recent years groups
of boys who seem to be a mixture of Yablonsky's social and

violent gangs have emerged. 'Skinheads', with a distinctive haircut and uniform, are quite racially prejudiced and will systematically set upon immigrants. 'Hells-angels' are another relatively well structured group, with a uniform, special membership criteria and initiation rites, who are basically a 'social gang' but seem easily provoked and often find themselves in violent situations.

Hooligans

Consideration of the modern teenage gang leads us straight on to the 'hooligan'. For most of us these are synonymous and we accept that hooliganism is mainly a group phenomenon. In a recent review of this subject Gibbens[118] defines hooliganism (a term derived from the name of a rough Irish family who lived in London at the turn of the century) as 'rowdy behaviour by groups, large and small, who cause a breach of the peace sometimes leading to actual violence to people'. He distinguishes between hooliganism and vandalism, the latter referring to 'wanton damage to property'. The phasic element of hooliganism interests Gibbens, for it seems that without obvious reason large aggregations of youths can occur, and such gatherings easily deteriorate into a kind of minor riot. The famous rock-and-roll riot in Copenhagen lasted for six days. He suggests two interrelated aspects of this type of hooliganism. First, the pleasure and satisfaction young people get from a large crowd —they can identify with it, they can feel powerful in a world that otherwise makes them feel helpless. Second, he feels that a number of 'troublemakers' (presumably the more overtly aggressive) can manipulate this crowd towards an objective the crowd would not otherwise have had.

Hooliganism brings us right back to the question of sanctioned and non-sanctioned violence. We can neatly define behaviour such as hooliganism but then *we* have defined it. Cohen[119] asks us to consider why vandalism and hooliganism are given such stereotyped images. He points out that deviance is not a static category; an act has to be defined and labelled as deviant by others. 'Vandals' (originally an east Germanic tribe who invaded western Europe in the fourth and fifth centuries and eventually sacked Rome in 455) conjure up barbarous, wilful, ignorant, reckless, restless, wanton, senseless destruction. Such judgements are, of course, made by one section of a community on another. The deviants would not accept such definitions themselves; for them the acts of destruction have sense and meaning. A good example of this is the Luddites of the early nineteenth century, who were making a deliberate protest. As Cohen indicates, if boys break into a school and smash it up, it is no help to call the behaviour 'wanton' and 'pointless'; it is better to find out why it happened and what it means. It is probably the boys' own school (not just a building at random) that has been entered and there are probably grievances within the school. 'The highest rates of school vandalism tend to occur in schools with obsolete facilities and equipment, low staff morale and high dissatisfaction and boredom among the pupils.' [119]

In his article Cohen goes on to suggest that in the 1960s, when vandalism was defined as something new and ever-increasing, its extent and seriousness were exaggerated. If the figures for persons found guilty of malicious damage to property and malicious damage are looked at for England and Wales during the 1960s, we find a fall from 18,018, representing 1.6 per cent of all offences in 1961 to 17,297 in 1967, representing 1.1 per cent of all offences. Cohen suggests that there are six main types of vandalism: (1) acquisitive vandalism, eg, breaking into telephone money boxes, (2) tactical vandalism, eg, breaking a window to get arrested and get a bed in prison, or drawing attention to a grievance, (3) ideological vandalism, eg, breaking the windows of an embassy of a distasteful regime or chalking up slogans, (4) vindictive vandalism, for revenge, (5) play vandalism, eg, to find who can shoot out the most street lamps, and (6) malicious vandalism, an expression of rage or frustration, often directed at symbolic middle-class property. Different elements can, of course, be combined. Cohen also asks us to consider similar types of 'permitted' damage that are not labelled vandalism, eg, student rag activities; and to remember that nearly two-thirds of vandals are adults, though most railway vandalism (placing objects on railway lines) is carried out by young children between 10 and 12 years old.

A contemporary illustration of the way in which the 'vandal', as defined by the larger social group, does not accept the label was given by a recent BBC programme in which a number of young men and women who had all been involved in some recent activity of a violent kind were interviewed. They admitted their inability to understand why many of their critics regarded all-out war against Fascism as justified in 1939-45, but moderately violent protest against Fascism as unjustified in 1970. They were, in fact, referring to their collective efforts to prevent the all-white South African team playing football in this country. A fascinating aspect of this kind of situation is that nearly all of us take sides—most of us were for or against the 'Stop the 70 Tour' campaign. It is exactly situations such as this which can, if social conditions allow, escalate into violent group conflict, each sub-group believing that it is *right* and the others are wrong and must be defeated. War stemming from this type of dispute may seem an exaggeration, but if we consider it in the terms just given, some warlike ingredients are to be found.

Football hooliganism is a contemporary problem in Britain, sometimes giving rise to mini-warfare on a Saturday afternoon. It also gave rise to so much public 'concern' that a team of researchers in Birmingham was asked to investigate the matter. In their preliminary report Harrington[82] and his team suggested that among the factors responsible was the feeling of identification with the team being supported, the glory or ignominy achieved by the team being shared by the spectator. Consequently, aggressive play on the field may be associated with disturbances on the terraces. Anger felt towards the referee or the opposing team may be displaced on to supporters

of the other club. 'We have good evidence that many middle-
aged, quiet and industrious men who are models of respect-
ability at home and at work undergo a temporary personality
transformation on Saturday afternoons and swear, shout and
boo, and argue with the spectators nearby.' One informant
went so far as to tell the investigator that all his inner tension
and anxieties disappeared when he was watching football.
Proportionally very few arrests are made for this type of hooliganism, but those that are arrested are males, usually aged
15-19 years, of low socio-ecomic status, and 54 per cent of
them have a previous conviction of some sort. Most of the
injuries sustained in the violence are minor and the damage
to trains is not a great economic problem; British Rail estimated damage to be about £5,000 per annum in Scotland and
£1,500 per annum in the rest of the country. Much of the
fighting is between rival groups after the game and there may
be recognisable feuds between supporters of specific clubs. As
with other violent situations, the carrying of weapons is
usually a symptom of fear but equally is a potent factor in the
escalation of violence. One factor the research team did not
discuss is transport. Recently, higher wages and faster, more
efficient public transport has meant that large numbers of
exuberant teenage supporters have been able to travel to away
matches, thus increasing the possibility of interaction between
rival fans.

Riots and Civil Disorder

Sometimes we are apt to believe the headlines and assume that
civil disorder and strife are more prevalent now than ever
before. Clearly there is plenty of room for improvement, but
we must not get things out of perspective. Every history book
indicates that as long as man has had a recorded history he has
indulged in riot and civil disorder. In other words, collective
violence is not unusual, not something to be astonished at;
this is not to say that it is desirable or inevitable, but that it is
commonplace. A review of the violent history of western

civilisation has been written by Tilly,[120] who reminds us of such events as the Wat Tyler rebellion of 1381, the German peasant wars of 1525, and the provincial insurrection against Henry VIII in 1536. In the same volume Taft and Ross[9] refer to the hundreds of deaths and thousands of serious injuries in American labour disputes, and the 160 occasions when troops have intervened. The commonest cause of all this violence was the denial of the right to organise through refusal to recognise a union.

Most writers who have examined civil disorders tend to endorse this kind of 'grievance' hypothesis. Gurr[121] talks of three levels of causation. Firstly, deprivation—induced discontent in which there is a discrepancy between what men feel they deserve and what they think they are capable of attaining. Then there is the attitude of the populace to the legitimacy of their political system, so that people who are contented with the political structure of their country are less likely to enter into civil strife than those who do not accept their government. Finally, the structural characteristics of the nation itself are important—the strength of the army, the police, etc. Countries where coercive forces are either small or relatively large seem to have the lowest levels of strife, but more important than size is the consistency with which coercion is employed.

Perhaps one of the most relevant and powerful pieces of evidence supporting the grievance hypothesis is the *Report* of the National Advisory Commission on Civil Disorders,[122] which was commissioned by President Johnson after the 1967 riots in several negro ghettos. This is one of the most important documents that has ever been produced in this field, for it sets out the details of the riots as seen very soon after the events, and draws bold conclusions which, while they may be embarrassing to the US Administration, are a remarkable tribute to the freedom of public enquiry in America.

The commission pointed to five 'powerful ingredients' in the black areas of American cities that acted as catalysts: (1)

frustrated hope generated by the civil rights struggle, (2) a climate heavy with the approval and encouragement of violence, (3) a frustrated feeling of powerlessness to change the system, (4) a new mood of self-esteem and enhanced racial pride, and (5) the view of the police as a symbol of white power, white racism, and white repression. In fact, as one reads through the report, it is clear that the commission points its finger in turn at all the factors we have considered so far in the causation of violence: frustration, paranoia, training, obedience to leaders (especially among the troops), anger, fear, etc. They discovered that virtually every major episode of urban violence that summer was foreshadowed by an accumulation of unresolved negro grievances. For example, in Atlanta there was a rapidly growing negro population which by 1967 formed 44 per cent of the whole but was scattered in several ghettoes. Some real-estate agents engaged in 'block-busting' (ie, putting a negro family into a previously all white area) to stimulate panic sales by whites. The town was full of marches and countermarches by civil-rights and white-supremacist organisations. In June 1967 the Ku Klux Klan marched through one of the poorer negro sections. In general, the negroes had poorer housing, poorer education, poorer jobs, and lower pay; and some firms advertised jobs by race. The riot was triggered by a series of events following informal negro residential meetings to discuss their grievances. A protest meeting was organised at which Stokely Carmichael, a militant black-power leader, spoke. Large numbers of police were deployed and Carmichael declared that there might have to be a riot if the police were not removed. He was arrested. The next day a negro youth started to hit a burglar alarm bell that was ringing, the police arrived, a scuffle ensued, a shot was fired and the youth was hurt. That evening Carmichael urged the negroes to take to the streets, and they did in hundreds. Carmichael announced to the press: 'It's not a question of law and order. We are not concerned with peace. We are concerned with the liberation of black people. We have to build a revolution.'

All in all the commission were very clear that social tensions between privileged and underprivileged, between black and white, were the basic problems. These culminated in the hot summer of 1967 in a national mood of anger, frustration and resentment among the negroes. In this atmosphere an incident trivial in itself set off a full-scale riot, and in every town they found such an incident.

In a situation of this kind almost everybody is induced to 'take sides'. President Johnson no doubt did his best to be impartial, but even as he set up the Commission of Inquiry into the riots he took sides in this kind of way: 'First let there be no mistake about it—the looting, arson, plunder and pillage which have occurred are not part of a civil rights protest. ... The criminals who committed these acts of violence against the people deserve to be punished—and they must be punished. Explanations have been offered, but nothing can excuse what they have done.'[122] In fact, the commission only found thousands of ordinary negroes living, usually in fear, often in squalor, always discriminated against in underprivileged circumstances. Caplan and Paige[123] published the findings of a survey of households in the riot areas of Detroit and Newark, the interviews being carried out by negroes. The 673 subjects were divided into rioters and non-rioters according to their participation in the violence. Both rioters and non-rioters were residents of the riot city, they had similarly low incomes and poor education. The rioters, however, tended to show more job dissatisfaction, were more conscious of racial discrimination, were more pro-black, anti-white, and anti-USA. In essence, they were very similar to the non-rioters but angrier.

In more recent times civil disorder has come to the United Kingdom in the form of violent unrest in Northern Ireland. Many of the ingredients are the same as with the American riots—economic deprivation of parts of the community; little or no representation of the minority groups (this time Catholics, instead of negroes) in the affairs of government; a long history of tense coexistence between two groups that see themselves as a group clearly distinguished from the 'others'; a civil-rights movement that was singularly unsuccessful in producing change; a police force seen by the minority to be an agent of the majority; a series of trigger events that produce violence which then escalates. Once this point has been reached, each group takes up an immovable position, as they did in the Blake and Mouton experiment. The IRA are freedom fighters to the Catholics and criminal gunmen to the Protestants, the British army are armed agents of tyranny to the Catholics and a peacekeeping force to the Protestants. It is extremely difficult for any politician or other interested person to see both sides of the question.

War

It is probably best to regard war as large scale and/or prolonged violent hostilities between two relatively well organised groups of people. In other words war emerges from other forms of group violence and is simply distinguished by its seriousness. It is the seriousness, the qualities of organisation, the scale, and the prolongation of the violence that give war its uniquely human aspects.

It is undoubtedly the most important kind of human violence. Numerically more people are killed by war than any other kind of violence. Furthermore, war raises the crucial ethical issues that confront us when we consider violence. Is war justified, and if so, when? Is all fair in war, or should we adhere to moral codes such as the Geneva Convention, which may somewhat limit our ability to win a fight we see as justified? During World War II the Japanese regarded it as reasonable to ill-treat prisoners of war because they regarded them as cowards who should have died for their country and they would have expected similar ill-treatment themselves had they been captured, but the Allies were angered by this attitude. In Northern Ireland the British authorities regard it as reasonable to intern militant Catholics without trial and interrogate them under duress, while the IRA regard bomb attacks on public buildings as justified. In each case the opposite side disagrees. These, then, are the kinds of dilemma we must bear in mind when we come to study the political aspects of war. Or, as Wright[124] puts it: 'The student of war must recognize that wishes, opinions, and beliefs, including his own, are among the phenomena with which he deals. He cannot exclude them from his predictive formulations as may the physicist'.

We shall consider the prevention of war in Chapter 9, but here concern ourselves with its basic phenomena, beginning with a look at its functions. In Chapter 2 it was suggested that the functions of violence may be regarded as concerned not only with direct competition between individuals, but especially with helping group social life to develop by providing spacing within the group, a commanding hierarchy and, by means of group defence, divided labour, so that individuals may be reared throughout a long period of immaturity. So violence in mammals is probably related to their gregarious habits. Naturally enough, most writers see the functions of war as simply an extension of the functions of violence in general: Wright, for example, regards 'group solidarity' in a political sense as the prime function of war, but also regards war as promoting change and disseminating one culture at the expense of another. Vayda[125] also sees war as performing this type of group function but rather more in terms of a defence against internal problems and tensions, as a 'flight' from the internal disharmony of the group; but he also mentions the purely competitive aspect of fighting, the redistribution of resources such as food and land, and the avenging of insults and thefts. Leeds,[126] in addition, considers that wars facilitate the internal and external adaptation of a group, by which he means more than group solidarity and the acquisition of resources. He looks at war and sees that it brings a number of massive benefits. It consolidates the internal power structure of the group concerned; it speeds technological and industrial change; antiquated norms are rapidly cast aside and values are re-examined; major reallocations of power and rewards occur within the society at war; labour is redistributed; social barriers are interfered with; and a wide diffusion of behaviour, know-how, and taste can take place. Perhaps even more fundamentally than all this, wide-scale genetic redistribution can occur and populations can disperse. Leeds suggests it is no accident that since World War II Europe has been prosperous as never before, national barriers within the Continent have become less important and we have now achieved a widespread Common Market. One could also speculate that World War II arose as a means (though unconscious) by which the German people could heal their internal dissensions, make their industry productive, and overcome some of the excessive humiliation to which they had been subjected.

One possible function of war, which very few writers seem to consider, is population control. In our peep at animal violence we considered overcrowding as a possible determinant of fighting (p25), and again, when we considered the social aspects of human violence (p73), crowding was acknowledged as a possible factor. On theoretical grounds it is just possible that war is both precipitated by overcrowding and a solution to it, though this is unlikely to be true in the straightforward sense, for very few population crashes coincide with wars[93] and increasing population can be accompanied by long periods of peace (eg, Scandinavia[92]). Nevertheless, as Richardson has calculated, between 1820 and 1949 some 67 million people died in wars, 300 of which were fought, causing $1\frac{1}{2}$-3 per cent of all human deaths.[92] Perhaps even more important than this are the indirect effects of war, for in their wake they can bring famine and disease. Richardson estimates that in the period he considered it is possible that some 10 per cent of all deaths were attributable to war, if one includes these secondary effects. Recent history has brought two tragic and startling examples of these secondary phenomena: both the civil war in Nigeria and the two wars in East Pakistan (Bangla Desh) brought colossal deathrates from the famine and disease consequent upon the wars and the disruption of communications, food supplies and housing.

It is difficult to be certain whether disturbances of this kind have a lasting biological effect and so provide another evolutionary function of war, but it seems quite possible that they do at times. If this is so, then we must ask ourselves whether we want to produce this type of biological effect (which may boil down to population reduction) by this kind of means? Are there not more humane and equally effective ways of achieving the same desirable, possibly inevitable, end?

How do wars start? If we return to the interaction model given in the Introduction (the car crash, p17), we can imagine that a combination of circumstances is required, and from what we have seen so far we can guess a number of the possible factors involved—group paranoia, internal dissension within a group or nation, social frustration and relative deprivation or humiliation, overcrowding, a closely organised hierarchy with obedient lower ranks, weapons that give a feeling of confidence of likely victory, and so on. This list is not exhaustive and not all the factors are active on any one occasion.

An interesting psychological study is the analysis of the start of World War I by Holsti.[127] This war is exceedingly well documented, and from an analysis of these documents Holsti comes to four conclusions. He suggests that as tension and stress increase in a crisis, then (1) time will be seen as increasingly important and decisions will become more and more concerned with the immediate future; (2) the range of alternatives open will be seen as fewer than those open to the enemy; (3) the range of alternatives will appear to become smaller while the enemy's range of alternatives will appear to become larger as time passes; and (4) communication channels will become overloaded and the information passed will become increasingly stereotyped, with a tendency to rely upon improvised methods of communication. As an illustration of these points Holsti quotes the Kaiser's despairing attitude on 30 July 1914: 'In view of the colossal war preparations of Russia now discovered, this is all too late, I fear. Begin! Now!' The Tsar, too, saw his own alternatives at that time as strictly limited: 'It is technically impossible to stop our military preparations which were obligatory owing to Austria's mobilization.' At the same time the Kaiser felt that the British could prevent the whole thing: 'He [Grey] knows perfectly well that if he were to say one single serious sharp and warning word at Paris and Petersburg, and were to warn them to remain neutral, both would become quiet at once. But he takes care not to speak the word, and threatens us instead! Common cur! England *alone* bears the responsibility for peace and war, and not we any longer!' While all this continued, messages between the monarchs were getting more frequent, more stereotyped and shorter. Communications became overloaded. The mean document length immediately following the assassination of Archduke Ferdinand was 326 words, but by the outbreak of war only 97 words.

Holsti has interpreted the psychology of this situation as indicating that because the time sense of the leaders was distorted they increasingly felt that time was running out and that they had to strike the first blow; further, the lack of accurate information about the potential enemy's intentions, movements, and military strength led to fear and paranoia— a feeling that the enemy has a bigger army, all the advantages and none of the justice. The present-day cold war between the big powers has many similar elements. Perhaps disaster is averted by an accurate transfer of information.

As a contrast to World War I, Holsti looks at the success of President Kennedy's tactics in the Cuban missile crisis. Given that the presence of missiles in Cuba created an international crisis (and that in itself is debatable) Kennedy adopted a number of very successful principles. Firstly, although he had to make the final decisions, he never took any before consultation and discussion; in the early stages he even refused to join the discussions, to allow a completely uninhibited exchange of opinions. Then at all stages he was careful to keep a number of options open for both sides: at no stage did he say, 'You must do this or we will attack', which could have forced the USSR into a 'lose face or have a war' situation. Thirdly, he did not press time factors, once or twice in fact deliberately prolonging decision-making periods. Lastly, he did not restrict himself to communicating by stiff formal diplomatic channels, but used all kinds of informal systems, including motor cyclists between the US and USSR embassies in London, and uncoded messages to his naval officers, to ensure that Mr Krushchev had the maximum amount of information on which to base his judgements.

We seem to be coming full circle because now we are dealing with the significance of the leadership in a crisis. Already in this chapter I have quoted writers who feel that a particular type of leadership can turn a tense group situation either into conflict or into constructive behaviour. In other words, although we are dealing with group matters, we are again emphasising the importance of the individual. Two illustrations from Holsti's contribution to a recent UNESCO meeting discussing human aggressiveness will make the point. A crucial decision in the events leading up to World War I was blind German support for Vienna's plan to punish Serbia. This decision was made by the Kaiser with almost no consultation. He went for a walk in the park with his chancellor and decided there and then. A similarly momentous decision was made in 1956 when John Foster Dulles decided, virtually alone, to cancel the loan to Egypt for the Aswan Dam. He adamantly refused even to consult the US ambassador to Egypt. Perhaps it is not surprising that Wright[124] has found that totalitarian nations tend to be more warlike.

All this indicates that in present-day politics some individuals have a very heavy burden of responsibility. Are we sure that the system of one man making these decisions is sensible? Is the health, wisdom, and knowledge of our leaders always sufficient for the task? In the United Kingdom three Prime Ministers since World War II have had to retire from active office through ill health and three Presidents of the United States have had serious illnesses while still in office.[128] One must not overdramatise the situation, and clearly no war could occur in the absence of a 'need' for the fight in at least one large group, but given that need as a predisposing factor, it is a salutary thought that whether armies march or not, whether bombs are dropped or not, depends upon the health and psychology of a very few individuals. If any reader is in doubt about the influence of one man on the conduct of war, let him read Churchill's *The Second World War*.

Before concluding this section on war we should perhaps recall one or two points made earlier in the book. War is almost exclusively a male activity, often aided and abetted by females, or even on very rare occasions directed by females, though never actually carried out by them. Many of the men in a war do not feel the personal emotions that would make them fight—in particular they are not angry—and so the leadership spends time and effort getting their soldier servants to feel persecuted by and prejudiced against the enemy. The whole exercise of the battle depends upon obedience and a great deal of a soldier's training is related to maximising this essential quality. Even so, men often have to be pressganged or conscripted or threatened with public disgrace to get them into the army in the first place.

Some maintain that group violence is on the increase. Whether this is true or not is almost impossible to discern because of the shortage of data. Richardson[92] suggests that there have been fewer but fiercer wars since 1820 than before. Maybe this increasing destructiveness is the very element that will cause us to shake war out of our evolutionary system—if our species survives long enough.

References to this chapter appear on pp186-7

7 *Violence in Disease*

By now the reader will have become aware that we cannot see violent acts in isolation; they usually occur in a social context, with social meaning and function. This means that, in general, two or more individuals are involved in violence, and not just in the sense of one being a giver and another a receiver; each individual contributes to the violence in a positive way. Clearly, then, it is a mistake to believe that violence is solely the product of one individual's disturbance or 'sickness'. On the other hand, we have seen in Chapters 3 and 4 that violence in man presupposes that he has a number of intricate physiological and psychological mechanisms present and intact. A reasonable corollary is that if any of these mechanisms are absent, distorted, or damaged, then a diminished or an increased potential for violence may result. In fact, men almost certainly vary in their potential for violence partly because of the efficiency and strength of the mechanisms we have discussed. Some individuals depart so far from the group norms in terms of their violence potential that we are persuaded to look for illness or disease. Often, though, we are persuaded wrongly, for an individual may well have been trained to be extremely violent or extremely non-violent, or he may be under such extremes of frustration and provocation that any normally functioning internal system would respond with a high degree of violence. Nevertheless, there are a few people whose violence behaviour is best accounted for by damaged physiological or psychological mechanisms, but let it be stressed that such individuals, while of considerable interest, are few and do not account for the bulk of violence we see in the world, nor do they pose the really serious threats to mankind.

Brain Damage

Chapter 3 indicated the importance of brain function in violent behaviour and also briefly described one or two animal experiments that showed how specific types of brain damage can produce increased aggressivity. None of these experiments exactly mimics the process of any human disease but diseases and injuries can and do produce specific lesions in the brain which are sometimes also accompanied by increased aggressivity. We saw on p47 that if the cerebral cortex (the outer grey matter) is removed from the brain of a cat, the cat becomes exceedingly irritable and prone to violence. If a man develops a degenerative disorder of his brain that especially damages the cerebral cortex, such as one of the dementias, then he, too, may become disinhibited, excessively irritable and prone to aggressive words or even assaultative behaviour under minor provocation. Dementia is usually, however, a pretty gross type of degeneration, leaving the individual incapable of much co-ordinated or determined activity (both necessary for effective violence) and, therefore, unrelated to the types of violence we are usually considering in this book. A similar type of phenomenon occurred in the 1920s after the pandemic of encephalitis lethargica,[129] when children who had been affected by this brain infection became both destructive and impulsive, and violent, sometimes murderous, acts were seen. The brain areas chiefly affected by this disease were the basal ganglia, the hypothalamus and parts of the limbic system (see p46).

Most of the attempts to relate violence to brain disease have been concerned with much smaller and more localised degrees of damage than either of these two examples. A survey of 105 murderers referred for a medical opinion carried out by Hill and Pond[130] in 1952 found that about half of them had abnormal EEGs, and in recent years there has been a growing body of opinion wishing to link minor abnormalities of the limbic system with violent outbursts. The authors of a recent book[131] have postulated a 'dyscontrol syndrome', which is basically a disorder of impulse control related to minor abnormalities in the limbic system, and manifests itself as assaultativeness, excessive drinking, impulsive sexual behaviour and reckless driving. Unfortunately, this is not a clearly defined syndrome because most of its manifestations are in part socially determined. Furthermore, the data to support this hypothesis are as yet rather flimsy, although one or two case histories are quoted by these authors. One of these concerned Julia, who had a brain infection following mumps at the age of two. The damage caused by the infection brought on epileptic fits at the age of ten. Before the age of twenty-one she had assaulted twelve people without provocation, the worst attack occurring when she was eighteen and at the cinema. She felt a wave of terror pass over her body, went to the ladies' lounge, took a small knife out of her handbag, looked into the mirror and saw the left side of her face as disfigured and evil. Just then another girl bumped into her and Julia stabbed the intruder through the heart. Medical examination revealed difficulties with her memory functions and her EEG (brainwave) pattern was abnormal. X-rays of her brain showed some tissue shrinkage in the right temporal area. Special electrodes were implanted in her right amygdala, which was then remotely stimulated. At one point Julia lashed out at the wall with an angry grimace. Both right and left amygdalae were destroyed by a neuro-surgeon in the hope that she would be improved. Two years after the operation she is reported as having had only two mild rage episodes. This type of neuro-surgery has also been carried out in Japan,[132] but clearly it is only suitable for specially selected patients after extensive investigation.

Another area of the brain specially implicated in impulse control is the frontal lobe (just behind the forehead). Numerous patients with damage in this area have been prone to assaultative behaviour under minor provocation.

Epilepsy

In Julia's case quoted above[131] it will be noted that she developed epileptic fits. Epilepsy is a kind of electrical storm in the brain which indicates an excessive electrical irritability of the brain tissues. All of us can have epileptic fits if we are stimulated sufficiently by an electric current, but those individuals who have spontaneous attacks have either been born with the excess irritability or, as in Julia's case, have suffered some form of brain damage. A kind of mythology has grown up that epileptic patients (about $\frac{1}{2}$ per cent of the British population) are specially liable to be violent. Now undoubtedly such phenomena as 'automatic crimes' committed during an unconscious epileptic phase do exist. In a recent survey of English prisons and Broadmoor Hospital two cases were found (both in the Hospital) of automatic violence during an epileptic seizure and another man (in prison)[133] who, while in hospital some years previously, attacked a nurse during an epileptic attack,[134] but these were the only cases found and such phenomena are extremely uncommon. In fact, the vast majority of the 5/1,000 epileptics in the population are perfectly ordinary law-abiding people doing ordinary jobs.

Depression

Let us turn from disorders of structural mechanisms to disorders of psychological mechanisms. When we are depressed, we may feel inferior and useless, and one way of dealing with these unacceptable ideas is to project the 'cause' for them on to someone or something else. 'Everything is going wrong, but it's not my fault (that would be too much to bear), it's *their* fault, *his* fault.' In other words, a depressed person may develop paranoid ideas and sometimes these can go on to incorrigible delusions. When we feel attacked, we tend to react by fighting back, trying to get the first blow in, and our reaction may be somewhat proportional to the strength of the feeling experienced. Depressed people sometimes do strike out at 'society', close relatives and so on. Sometimes in a minor way by some small anti-social act (eg, shoplifting) but also on occasions by actual physical assault or even homicide.

Feelings of inadequacy, inferiority, misery and pessimism, which are part and parcel of the depressed mood, can convince many sufferers that they are no longer worthy to live, or that they would be better off dead. Suicide is not often considered as part of the problem of violence, but violent it surely is, and it may well be uniquely human violence. One of the common determinants of suicide is the depressed mood. Sometimes a person who wishes to commit suicide wishes to put other people out of their misery also. Some of the more horrible multiple murders have this kind of basis. A man who feels desperate, worthless and guilty may shoot his family and then try to kill himself. A suicidal woman in a desperate moment may shut the doors and windows, turn on the gas, and persuade her children to lie down beside her.

Child murder is perhaps especially likely to occur during the first few weeks or months of life at the hands of a mother who is affected with a puerperal depression brought about by the hormonal and psychological changes that occur at the time of childbirth. This type of murder has for a long time been put into a special legal category.

Numerous writers have noted the close association between homicide and suicide,[135, 136] and in the United Kingdom approximately one-third of all murders kill themselves after the crime.[137] Some writers[95] have noted an inverse relation between homicide rates and suicide rates in any given culture or community. This perhaps fits with the psychoanalytic notion that depression is a turning inwards of aggressive impulses. Kendell[138] has looked at this notion in a slightly modified form and found that the scanty data available does lend some support to the idea that depression is caused by the inhibition of aggressive responses to frustration: for example, the Hutterites (an Anabaptist sect with about 9,000 members living in small agricultural communities in North America) have a very low level of murder and assault but a high level of depression.

Whatever the theories and explanations there is little doubt about an association between aggression in its various forms and depression, even though it should be emphasised that most violent acts are not carried out on the basis of depression and most depressive patients are in no way violent.

Schizophrenia

Schizophrenia is a very unpleasant psychotic illness that probably comes closer to the layman's impression of insanity than does depression. The schizophrenic person sometimes harbours a number of paranoid delusions, believing that he is being persecuted; he may also believe that someone is interfering with his mind, or that God has given him a special mission, and he may hear voices that talk about him or give him instructions. As with the depressed patient with paranoid ideas, it is possible for him to deal with his persecutors in a violent way, and if he hears a voice instructing him to kill someone he may act upon that instruction.

Perhaps the most famous of all schizophrenic murderers is the unfortunate M'Naughton, who found notoriety and immortality when his case caused so much political controversy in 1843. The full story is masterfully set out in Walker's *Crime and Insanity in England*[139] but, in brief, he shot Sir Robert Peel's private secretary, in mistake for the Prime Minister, as he suffered from the delusion that he was being victimised by Tories. The jury committed him to Bethlem Hospital under a special verdict, but the public, parliament and of course *The Times* were not satisfied and the House of Lords was asked a number of questions about the law surrounding this type of case, and the answers given have become enshrined as the M'Naughton rules.

Some of the more 'motiveless' murders of our own time have been carried out by schizophrenics. It is even possible that the murdered President Kennedy and his brother Senator Robert Kennedy were shot by schizophrenic men; certainly both assassins seemed to have firmly fixed paranoid ideas. Rothstein[140] studied ten patients who had been admitted to the US Center for Federal Prisoners because of threats to the life of the President of the United States, and all ten were suffering from schizophrenia.

Once again, however, it must be emphasised that schizophrenia (which is a common disease, affecting nearly 1 per cent of the population) is only very infrequently followed by any kind of violence. Violent criminals, soldiers, lawyers, politicians are not all schizophrenics! In fact, Brennan[141] recently reported that patients who had been in mental hospitals had a lower than average conviction rate for all offences, including violent offences.

Morbid Jealousy

A special symptom of mental illness that can be the result of almost any known type of psychiatric disease is morbid jealousy. This is of particular importance because a great deal of violent crime is related to family and domestic quarrels and morbid jealousy can produce fights, even death. Michael Shepherd[142] reviewed this topic and studied eighty cases. Usually the symptom appears in one partner of a marriage who wrongly believes that his or her spouse has been unfaithful. This belief can be held with absolute conviction, the patient spending enormous time and effort furnishing evidence of the infidelity. Whatever happens, he or she cannot be shaken from the mistaken belief, and paroxysms of rage sometimes end in assault or suicidal action. The types of psychiatric syndromes that can produce this symptom are alcoholism, dementia and other forms of brain disease, schizophrenia, depression, and personality disorder. The classic example of morbid jealousy in the English literature is Othello, and the reader will remember that the story ended in violence, with a homicide and a suicide.

Psychopathic Personality Disorder

Earlier chapters of this book have stressed the gregarious nature of man, and, indeed, we are probably more interdependent than most creatures and our 'success' as a species is related to this interdependence. Now we are not born as a socialised animal, we are born helpless and dependent. The social skills of living with our fellow men, considering their needs as well as our own, of giving and taking, of sublimating personal desires for the benefit of the group as a whole, all have to be learned. Many writers have suggested that we are born with a basic temperament that has an important influence on the way we learn these social skills and the way our personality finally unfolds, but all are agreed on the importance of learning as we progress from infancy to adulthood.

Clearly, then, if the learning process is unsatisfactory or distorted in some way, it is quite possible for us to end up as adults who have none of the social skills we need. The already mentioned Harlows experiment[33] demonstrated that totally depriving rhesus monkeys of their parents and peers turned them into asocial, untamable, ineffective, aggressive creatures who fought one another and could not even reproduce their own kind. Some would say that the Harlows had produced psychopathic rhesus monkeys, because in human beings we tend to call this marked absence of social skills, especially if it is accompanied by anti-social behaviour, psychopathic behaviour. The term is highly unsatisfactory, because it is rather ill defined and has crept into the vernacular as a term of abuse. In the United States of America it is hardly ever used in the technical sense, sociopath being the preferred term there. These different terms perhaps indicate a difference of emphasis, the British view looking more at the underlying psychological dysfunction and the American more at the behavioural manifestations. Henderson,[143] described psychopaths as people who are cold and indifferent to others, egocentric, emotionally unstable and subject to episodes of psychoneurosis. Other characteristics which have been attributed to this group are impulsiveness, lack of foresight, a malfunctioning conscience, over-reactiveness to stress and most centrally of all an inability to give and take love. This last feature, which could lie behind most of the others mentioned, is clearly very damaging to a creature who needs to relate to others all day and every day.

Some authorities dispute whether the syndrome just described is a disease at all. Well it certainly is a 'dis-ease', for people who are at constant loggerheads with all and sundry are exceedingly miserable, but it is clearly not an illness in the episodic sense that pneumonia or depression are illnesses. Robins[144] demonstrated the persistence of the disorder from childhood to adulthood, and also showed that it runs in families and carries a poor prognosis, with early death being commonplace, due to self-neglect, fighting, careless accidents, the effects of too much alcohol and other drugs, suicide, etc. Increasingly the disturbances subsumed under the umbrella of psychopathic disorder are being regarded as diseases, and are being sent in increasing numbers to physicians. This dismays the doctors somewhat, because they have no curative treatments available nor facilities for managing the patients sent.

The psychopath never fits into his surroundings, culture, society or group. All his attempts at close personal relationships end in disaster or rejection. Not surprisingly he is apt to think people are against him, and he is frequently angry. Added to this he is impetuous, and violent assault becomes part of his behaviour pattern. One or two psychopathic life stories have been well documented in recent years and illustrate very well the difficulties that arise and the violence that can arise from them. In *Born to Trouble*[145] Harry, a psychopath, is conceived by a brutal sadistic father and a vagrant ineffective teenage girl. His mother rears him in the most calamitous circumstances, and as soon as he is old enough he becomes a lawbreaker. Throughout his life he finds all relationships difficult, those with women especially difficult, and he assaults quite a number of females, sometimes under very minor provocation, sometimes without provocation at all. An illustration of his over-reactivity is given by his teenage response to a girl he wants as a friend but who does not share his desires. She avoided him by breaking dates so he planned not just to have it out with her, but to *kill* her, and bought himself a special knife for the job. Being a psychopath, Harry is ineffective in everything he does and the planned murder is no exception. It goes wrong. He spends most of his life going in and out of gaol and he dies at the early age of thirty-nine by swallowing five open safety pins.

Because his impetuosity is coupled with an astonishing inability to succeed, the psychopath is a common frequenter of prisons. In a recent American survey[146] sociopathy was estimated as being present in some 56-81 per cent of convicted felons. Because of their basic insecurity, their self-centred immediate needs, their fears of other people, their low threshhold to frustration, and often their violent brutalising childhood, they are liable to act violently in situations that would not precipitate violence in other people.

XYY Syndrome

This interesting and yet insignificant genetic problem must be mentioned because of the immense public interest it engenders. The genetic material that constitutes the biological memory, enabling the first cell formed at conception to develop into a complex living structure, is carried by a number of intracellular bodies called chromosomes. In man we have forty-six of these, twenty-three coming from our mother and twenty-three from our father. Two of the forty-six are concerned with gender determination and there are two varieties of gender or sex chromosomes, labelled X and Y.

A foetus with two X chromosomes becomes a female and a foetus with an X and a Y becomes a male. Chromosomal abnormalities of all kinds can occur, and it is possible for a living person to lack a sex chromosome or to have an extra one or two chromosomes. Our understanding of these problems has increased enormously in the past ten or twenty years, and only quite recently the abnormality of a double Y chromosome (XYY) was discovered.[147] At first it was realised that such patients are especially likely to be tall and perhaps slightly below average in intelligence. By the mid-1960s, however, the special hospitals of Britain where mentally subnormal criminals are detained were found to have yielded a crop of such cases.[148] This discovery produced an immediate speculation that the XYY syndrome and criminality were associated. Moreover, because one or two aggressive patients with the abnormality were noted, an association was thought to exist between XYY and violence. Intense public interest turned to the subject and in a BBC television programme one normally temperate observer rated the discovery of the XYY syndrome as 'the greatest breakthrough in criminology of this century' and another suggested that a major cause of crime had been discovered.

It is fascinating how we seem to need a simple physical, preferably genetic, explanation for 'nasty' behaviour such as crime and violence. Presumably if we could really see 'the cause' of violence down the end of a microscope, then we would be guiltless, totally exonerated. The violence would be the fault of biology, nothing to do with us and the way we have constructed our society. In fact, things are rather different, for in a recent review of the work relating to several sex chromosome abnormalities, including the XYY syndrome, Casey and his colleagues[149] have shown that 'an extra set of chromosomes, whether X or Y, is not a major factor of itself in predetermining delinquency but only when present in combination with mental subnormality and adverse family background'.

Alcoholism

Again and again it has been demonstrated that excessive alcohol intake is associated with violence: [150] for example, road accidents,[151, 152] homicide[153, 154, 155] and lesser crimes of violence.[156] Although it is as yet impossible to determine whether the association is causative, or simply present because violence and heavy drinking are both related to a third more important factor—social class, for example[153]—I think we are justified in considering the two main theoretical reasons why individual violence should be associated with alcohol. Firstly, there is the pharmacological action of the drug itself: it is a sedative and it particularly sedates those so-called 'higher' brain functions which we have spent so much time training and which are so essential for proper social interaction— our inhibitions. Earlier in this chapter we saw that some workers suggest that damage to the brain can produce 'dyscontrol', a lowered frustration tolerance, increased impulsiveness and decreased thoughtful appraisal of problems. Perhaps a similar but temporary effect can be obtained by a sedative intoxicant, and alcohol is the one on sale to the general public. Consequently, if we meet a frustrating or aggression-provoking situation when we have taken a fair dose of alcohol, we may be more liable to resort to actual violence than when we are sober. Another way of looking at this action is to see how subjects under experimental conditions respond to rewards and punishments. Vogel-Sprott[157] has found that under conflict subjects who have taken alcohol tend not to be bothered by the inhibitory effect of future punishment, but they are just as stimulated by the prospects of reward.

Our second consideration should be the disease of alcoholism itself. We can for our purposes here regard alcoholism as including any type of excessive drinking which is beyond the requirements of ordinary social mores and which produces either physical or social deterioration. By social deterioration I mean excessive expenditure so that essential purchases are neglected, an inability to carry out efficient employment, and interference with social interaction, especially marital inter-actions. Alcohol is a particularly good sedative; since it is socially acceptable, its use does not carry a connotation of mental fragility, and it is freely available. The people who use alcohol in a persistent and excessive manner are often those with anxieties and problems they wish calmed, those who find life more acceptable when its edges are blurred. Patients with mental illnesses such as depression and schizo-phrenia can sometimes find themselves in this category. If they do, it is quite possible for their difficulties to be pro-longed, by reason of the excessive drinking, beyond the orig-inal problem they attempted to wash away with the drink. An especially vulnerable group comprises people with life-long personality and social-adjustment problems, and the so-called psychopaths are a good example of this group. Inevit-ably a high proportion of psychopathic people turn to drink and become alcoholics. In essence, therefore, we will end up with a group of people who are already unusually prone to violent outbursts, taking on the additional problems of drunk-enness, with its reduction of inhibitions and interference with considered judgements. We have, then, a good theoretical basis for the association between alcoholism and violence.

Nevertheless, let us not forget one of Wolfgang's[158] points. Although alcohol may be present in a high proportion of violent offenders and their victims, this is not to say that a high proportion of drunkards or alcoholics will be violent offenders. Furthermore, we must remember with Shakespeare that alcohol not only suppresses inhibitions it interferes with function: 'It provokes and unprovokes, it provokes the desire but takes away the performance' (*Macbeth*). Gibbens and Silberman[156] have suggested that assaulting may be provoked by drink, but serious assault may be made less likely because of the concommitant motor difficulties.

Other Addictive Drugs

Three serious difficulties present themselves when we consider other addictive drugs. Firstly, they are relatively new on the scene and much less studied; hence we have to rely more on impression and less on data. Secondly, we tend to talk of 'drugs' as a homogeneous entity, whereas in reality there are a number of different substances that are abused and each needs to be considered in its own right. Thirdly, drug-abusers tend to take several different substances at the same time, producing a variety of possible effects.

Having said all this there are one or two similarities with the alcohol problem just described. A number of 'drugs' have sedative actions—for example, barbiturates and narcotics—and many of them are used by people to obtain relief from their mental anxieties and strains, to blur the edges of life in the same way that the alcoholic uses his drug. To some extent there is an either/or relationship between alcohol and some drugs, for certain individuals with persistent psychological and social disturbances turn to the former and others to the latter, the choice depending upon such factors as availability, age, cultural pressure and so on. For my part, therefore, I would expect some similarities between the behavioural characteristics of the alcohol-abuser and of the drug-abuser.

The best recent review of the association between drugs and violence has been given by Tinklenberg and Stillman,[159] though it is clear from their article how little we really know. *Narcotics* such as heroin and morphine are described by some as having a tranquillising or calming effect, whereas a senior New York police officer, pleading for a medical rather than a criminal approach to the problem, said on television recently that a great deal of the violence in his city—robberies and muggings—is due to the heroin addict who in his desperation for the next 'shot' will do anything to get the money to buy it on the black market. A recent survey at my own hospital has suggested that heroin addicts are slightly more likely to have previous criminal convictions for violence than other kinds of addicts.[160] It may well be that, pharmacologically, heroin does induce tranquillity but that the frustration of insufficient supplies or the physical effects of the withdrawal symptoms themselves may induce anger and violence. Equally, we should remember that the heroin-addicted population is a highly selected one and may be prone to violence before the addiction starts.

Barbiturates are in their effects closer to alcohol than any of the other drugs under consideration in this section; but, if anything, a person intoxicated with barbiturates is less irritable and prone to violence than one intoxicated with alcohol. *Amphetamines*, on the other hand, are stimulants, used by the abuser to elevate mood, produce alertness, wakefulness, and increase performance. Long-distance lorry drivers and jazz drummers are common abusers. Unfortunately these substances can induce intense irritability and paranoia to the point of persecutory delusions, and in this way they are associated with violence. Again, however, we must be careful in drawing sweeping conclusions. It may be that people without personality problems who use the drugs simply for wakefulness have very different reactions to those of the addict, who is trying to construct a new world better than the ghastly reality he finds himself in. I know of one severely psychopathic man who is extremely violent when he takes alcohol but much more passive when he switches to amphetamines.

LSD and other psychotomimetics (such as mescaline) are very powerful inducers of disturbed consciousness, producing the most bizarre distortions of time sense, body image and visual perception. There is very little evidence of a consistently increased association with violence, although occasionally bizarre 'accidents' occur when, for example, a deluded subject may jump through a window convinced that he has acquired the power to fly. Also an occasional murder has been committed under the influence of LSD.

Marihuana, cannabis or hashish is in a rather different category to the other substances we have considered. Its pharmacological actions, which are ill understood, seem to be variable and much less intense; usually it is taken by smoking, and, most important of all, it is an accepted drug for a large and growing section of the community. It has to be given special consideration in a book on violence because of the supposed association, in the Middle East, of hashish and homicide (our word assassin is derived from the Arabic for hashish-eater). The best recent review of the effects of cannabis is that by Lewis,[161] who emphasises the lack of hard data and the discrepancies between the published reports. Among the clinical features of special interest he finds 'heightened suggestibility' as a probable explanation for the variety of behaviour reputed to have been induced by cannabis.

Lewis's conclusion about the relation of cannabis to violence is a pertinent one with which to close this whole section, for it could be applied to any of the drugs, including alcohol, which we have considered.

> The most likely relation that emerges from the welter of conflicting statements is that chronic or excessive indulgence ... may, in some people—a small minority of the male public at risk—lead to attacks of disturbed consciousness, excitement, agitation or panic, and reduce self control. The extent to which the affected person may commit a crime in this state of mind depends more on his personality than on the dose or preparation ... which he has been taking.

Suicide

This topic might not be expected to appear in a book on violence, and yet it is difficult to leave it out, because it certainly constitutes a form of violence, although largely self-directed. It is not entirely self-directed, for, as we have already seen in this chapter, suicide and homicide can go hand in hand, and it is probably true to say that there is never an absolutely pure suicide motive, some of the aggression always seeming to be directed at the outside world as well. The wife or lover who kills herself often hurts her partner more by this act than by any other she could possibly undertake.

For further reference the reader is recommended to read

some of the standard works on the subject—Stengel,[162] Sainsbury,[163] and Menninger.[164] Suicide is frequently associated with disease though it can occur, of course, in the absence of disease, and it would be stretching our concept of disease a long way to consider the highly trained Japanese kamikaze pilots of World War II, or Captain Oates' self-sacrifice in Antarctica as 'diseased'. This type of action is much nearer to Durkheim's[97] concept of 'altruistic suicide', carried out for the benefit of the group. It was Durkheim, of course, who originally put forward the notion of 'anomie' or normlessness (see p78), which he specially related to suicide.

Even so, in our own culture, a good deal of suicide is related to disease, and it is precisely related to those diseases which we have seen are especially related to other forms of violence —brain damage, epilepsy, depression, schizophrenia, personality disorder, alcoholism and drug addiction.

Phenomenologically, homicide is related to suicide, and the two frequently occur together.[135] Statistically, suicide is a much more important form of violent death than homicide, thirty-three times as common in England and Wales; or, as Blom-Cooper[165] has indicated, between 1900 and 1950 there were some 7,500 murders known to the police but the suicide rate was running at something like 5,000 *per year*. In itself it is psychologically interesting that murder attracts more public concern and attention than most forms of death. The attention is not entirely rational. The figures just quoted indicate that one is much more likely to die by one's own hand than someone else's, and, as we shall see in Chapter 8, there are statistically more important forms of homicide.

Homicidal Threats

Despite the figures just given, it is paradoxical that, while murder generates more emotion and newsprint within society than suicide, society makes greater attempts to prevent suicide than murder. Outpatient services are provided, doctors lend a sympathetic ear and in appropriate cases will institute treatment, and voluntary bodies such as the Samaritans aim specifically at the threatened suicide. On the other hand, society's action in respect of homicide is largely concerned with measures after the tragedy has occurred—death penalties, imprisonment and the like. This would be reasonable if homicide was never preventable, but the facts state otherwise. As MacDonald[166] has recently indicated, homicide is frequently heralded either by a plea for help or a definite homicidal threat. In his book MacDonald tells of the Texan student who killed his mother, his wife and then shot forty-four people from a tower, killing fourteen of them. Five months before this incident he had told his psychiatrist that he was 'thinking about going up on the tower with a deer rifle and start shooting people', and then he failed to keep further appointments.

Recently a man came to my own outpatients' clinic threatening to do 'something desperate'. Try as I would I could not get him into a hospital because he showed very few signs of mental illness and in any case had failed to respond to hospital treatment in the past. No other asylum facilities were available for him and he had to be continued as an outpatient. During the next week he started four fires, one of these serious. Fortunately nobody was injured, but a homicide could well have resulted. MacDonald makes a plea for the homicidal threat to be taken as seriously as the suicidal threat, and for facilities to be set up to protect and assist people at moments of crisis; he calls them homicide-prevention centres, but hospitals, social work centres and police departments could establish such arrangements with a minimum of modifications.[167]

References to this chapter appear on pp187-9

8 *Violent Crime*

'Violent crimes have risen another 10 per cent' scream the headlines—commonplace contemporary journalism. The television programmes that follow each new set of figures always start from the premise that, year by year, we are being increasingly menaced by a growing band of thugs, hooligans, robbers and so forth, but most of us in Britain still live our lives without much first-hand contact with violent crime and are able to walk the streets of London without too much fear of assault. As the quotation on p19 has already suggested, a historical analysis of violence would suggest that this has not always been so. In fact, history makes it pretty clear that, compared with the last few previous centuries, the twentieth century is, for Western Civilisation, an age of law and order. (In terms of our previous thoughts on obedience, perhaps that is one of the reasons why it is also an era of large-scale wars.) How then are we going to interpret the statistics?

Unfortunately, there is no simple answer to this question. Firstly, short-term comparisons between one year and the next are not very meaningful, for even a decade is a very short period over which to observe changes in a society. If we are observing our weight, day-to-day, even week-to-week, fluctuations are not specially significant, since it is the trend over several weeks that counts. As far as crime is concerned, there is no argument whatsoever that since World War II the *figures* both in absolute terms and in proportion to the population have increased. For details of the statistical trends the reader should refer to the *Criminal Statistics* published by the Home Office in England, and to the *Uniform Crime Reports* of the USA. In Britain the figures for 'violent crimes against the person' have gone up much faster than any other type of crime, although murder rates have remained remarkably steady and low for fifty years or more. A detailed statistical analysis is not pertinent here but a few of the English figures (Table 1) should illustrate the point.

Table 1   Total numbers of violent crimes (indictable offences) known to the police in England & Wales

Annual Average

	1955-9	1960-4	1965-9	1970
Murder	149	156	185	186
Attempted murder	169	202	266	340
Threat to murder	56	71	101	90
Manslaughter	122	114	177	181
Infanticide	20	19	22	26
Child destruction	1	1	2	0
Causing death by dangerous driving	231	489	658	685
Wounding—endangering life	1,395	1,913	2,436	2,956
Other wounding	8,210	15,239	25,479	35,779
Assault	182	357	494	531
Rape	396	486	732	884

Home Office. *Criminal Statistics, England and Wales*, Cmnd 4708 (HMSO, 1971)

Usually we think of criminals as people other than ourselves, and sometimes we think of 'criminals' as being a limited term synonymous with prisoners. Consequently, we tend to forget that the official statistics deal with those lawbreakers who have both offended against the law and been brought to court. We also forget that, in England, by the time we die some 32 per cent will have been convicted of an indictable offence (ie, a serious offence).[168] A public opinion poll on the definition of 'violent crime' would be a most interesting exercise. Many people would probably define it in terms of *serious* interpersonal violence and would mainly think of violence combined with theft or bizarre sexual assaults. The reality is that the statistics, on the whole, are reflecting fighting behaviour between angry people, and most violent behaviour takes place in bars, cafés and homes.

In his study of crimes of violence McLintock[169] discovered that approximately 90 per cent of all recorded offences against the person were woundings, one half of the recorded crimes occurred in and around cafés and pubs, and family and domestic disputes accounted for another third. Another way of looking at the problem is to realise that nearly half the offenders and victims knew one another. None of this should surprise us at this stage of this book, nor should the finding that the majority of the fights were between males, and that, of the female victims, three-quarters were attacked by relatives or close neighbours. Half the victims required some form of hospital treatment but, as this was a British survey where firearms are only rarely used in violence, only 20 per cent were detained in hospital. In other words, McLintock's study does not confirm the stereotyped view of the violent crime scene.

Even in the United States, where violent crime is considered to be much commoner than in Britain, some of the same considerations apply. As Morris and Hawkins wrote recently,[170] 'taken together, murders involving spouse killing spouse, parent killing child, other family killings, romantic triangles and lovers' quarrels, and arguments between those previously acquainted with one another account for 80% of all homicides in America. You are safer on the streets than at home; safer with a stranger than with a friend or relative'. A further aspect of American violent crime which these authors draw attention to and which is often forgotten is that the homicide rate has declined since the 1930s.

The legal categories quoted in the figures are, of course, crucial. How many British readers realise that most of those startling soaring graphs published every year to illustrate the increase in violent crime are based on the official figures for violence against the person and do not include robbery with violence, the figures for which are dealt with in the official statistics under offences against property. Much more fundamental than this even is the type of category into which a particular violent incident is put by the police and the courts. Walker illustrates this point neatly in his textbook[171] by showing how a domestic quarrel in which a husband attacks his wife with a hammer could end up in any of several categories:

> The choice of heading would be made by the police after their initial enquiries... Thus the husband who could be proved to have said before hitting his wife 'I am going to kill you' might well be recorded as an attempted murder; if he kept his mouth shut, or if his words went unheard, he would probably not. If his blow fractured her skull it would probably be recorded as felonious wounding; if it merely rendered her unconscious, as a malicious wounding, or even a mere indictable assault. If she successfully dodged it, it might well be treated as a non-indictable assault. Moreover, from the clinical observer's point of view it is fallacious to distinguish even murder from crimes of this sort, since often it is mere accident that determines whether an attempted murder succeeds or whether a blow that was merely intended to inflict serious harm has fatal results.

Perhaps the most important consideration of all in interpreting violence statistics is hidden within this little illustration, and that is the question of whether the incident is reported or not. Clearly, if the wife had been killed or nearly killed, police action would have been almost inevitable, but it is doubtful whether lesser forms of injury would be reported to the authorities. Reporting would depend partly on whether the wife needed to go to hospital, whether she herself saw the police as being able to assist her, or whether, indeed, she felt she needed assistance. Neighbours can and sometimes do call the police to domestic fights of this kind, but the police are often reluctant to intervene unless an actual and serious injury has occurred. The other common type of violent crime—the street fight—is also subject to exactly the same kind of filtering processes before it gets into the official statistics. Consequently, we have in any country a great deal of unlawful violent behaviour that never comes to official attention. Because it is unreported crime we have no idea at all how much of it actually occurs, and yet the size of the unreported element is crucial in arguments about the extent and trend of any particular offence behaviour.

The historical quotations given so far have perhaps tended to imply that violent crime is on the decrease and yet, as I have already indicated, violent crime statistics seem to say that reported violence is on the increase. Are these different observations compatible? Let me answer by reference to a hypothetical island. This island has a population of 1 million and an exactly balanced birthrate and deathrate so that it always remains at 1 million. Now the actual number of violent incidents on the island remains for some years at exactly 10,000, but only 30 per cent or 3,000 of these are reported and find their way into the published statistics. One year, however, there begins a campaign against violence or, for some reason, the people of the island have become less tolerant of violence. Two things happen as a consequence: the number of violent incidents diminishes and the percentage of those incidents reported increases. After five years we reach a new equilibrium in which the number of violent incidents has gone down to 9,000 but the percentage reported has gone up to 50 per cent or 4,500. The official statistics, therefore, show an increase in reported crimes of violence from 3,000 to 4,500, or 1,500 more incidents/million/year—a 50 per cent increase. Just imagine the glee with which the prophets of doom could draw their soaring graphs, when in absolute (and once you leave a hypothetical island—unmeasurable) terms the number of violent incidents has fallen by 1,000/million or 10 per cent.

In his study of violence, McLintock[169] indicated that there was strong evidence from interviews with older police officers that, in the past, a considerable amount of violent behaviour had been taken for granted and not reported to or recorded by the police. Furthermore, even simple administrative changes in police methods of recording would, by themselves, have caused an apparent increase of 13 per cent between 1939 and 1960. Some Scottish doctors who know Glasgow well pointed out to me recently that one of the important factors in the recent wave of gang violence in that city was the rehousing of many of the slum tenants. In their old areas Saturday night brawls and knife fights were largely tolerated, but in their new and more middle-class surroundings concerted police action has brought a large proportion of the fighting youths to book.

Caution is necessary, therefore, in interpreting the statistics, but I am ready to accept fairly straightforward anecdotal evidence from police officers and the like that some forms of violence have increased in recent years. Robbery is one of those offences and McLintock suggested that in Britain others might be 'hooliganism' (see p93), violent sexual crime, and racial antagonism towards both Irish and coloured immigrants. Rates and trends do not seem all that important to me except insofar as they create public opinion. This problem may be especially acute in America. It is perhaps significant that during the 1968 Presidential campaign a *New York Times* reporter found that the citizens of Garnett, Kansas, were up in arms about crime, but in their own town there had not been a rape for 12 years, nor a murder for 21 years, and the only person in jail there was a seventeen-year-old hotrodder! [172]

This last point only serves to emphasise that the amount of crime of any kind can differ to a great extent locally. The British figures for crime are not spread evenly throughout the country—in fact, there are marked differences between rural England and London, and in recent times Northern Ireland has seen violence on a large scale. The Glasgow problem is different from the Birmingham problem. Surely this is another good reason for not reading too much into short-term fluctuations of nationally reported crime.

Violence by Car

Earlier (p42) I emphasised how important the nature of the available weapon is to man in his violence behaviour. All too often we forget that the car is a very dangerous weapon; it is lethal, it is readily available, violent behaviour with it carries very little stigma or sanction, and it is possible to be violent in a car without it being obvious that violence is occurring. After all 'accidents will happen'.

The simple comparative deaths rates shown in Table 2 will put this problem in perspective, especially when we realise that almost half the court work of Great Britain is concerned with motoring offenders.

Table 2   Deaths by violence in England & Wales—1972

Accidents	
Motor transport	6,869
Other „	358
Poisoning	951
Falls	5,633
Burning	792
Other	2,670
Suicide	3,939
Homicide and war	350

Whitaker's Almanack, 1972

Parry in his book *Aggression on the Road*[173] produced some vivid and frightening profiles of motorists. He tested the hypothesis that aggressive drivers and anxious or frightened drivers are more likely to have an accident than other drivers. By giving questionnaires to a randomly selected group of car drivers he found that quite a high proportion admitted to aggressive behaviour such as chasing another vehicle when annoyed, driving straight at another vehicle in anger, deliberately trying to edge another car off the road, and fighting with other drivers. These aggressive tendencies tended to diminish with age, and the aggressive feelings were correlated with the number of accidents. Combinations of high aggression and high anxiety made for an even greater degree of accident liability. Parry gives some profiles that come from a series of interviews he conducted with drivers who had admitted to aggressive behaviour. A couple are worth repeating here.

Male, aged 28, one serious and two minor accidents; an accountant

I have never actually edged another car right off the road but, to be perfectly honest, I have tried on a few occasions. Why? Because I get annoyed or to teach someone a lesson. I remember once, about 6 months ago, being followed by this bloke with his car headlamps fully on. I thought at first he wanted to overtake me, so I pulled over to the side to let him pass—he didn't. In fact, every time I allowed him to overtake he slowed down as I did. Eventually I became so annoyed I pulled up, thinking he would also stop. He carried on and as the car passed mine I noticed three blokes, all about twenty or so, were in it. They hooted at me, gave me the V sign and drove off. I was pretty annoyed, so I chased after them and gave them the same treatment. It developed into a running battle, and at one point I drove up alongside and gradually crowded their car into the dirt

Male, aged 26, one serious and one very serious accident; a shipping clerk

Everything went wrong that day, I had a row with one of the other clerks about an invoice or something and then after work I found I'd been given a £2 ticket for parking my car to cause obstruction. One thing and another, the rush hour got on my nerves. Then, when I was almost home, following slowly behind a line of traffic, the car in front stopped and the chap decided to park there with a whole lot of cars behind him. I was furious and tooted him, but he waved me on, telling me to drive round his car. People (drivers) behind were also tooting, but he started walking away, so I drove my car right into the back of his. Luckily, there was no one inside his car because the boot and rear bumper were badly dented. My nearside headlamp was also smashed. The man came running back and tried to drag me out of my car but a few other drivers from behind got out and pulled him away.

These interviews illustrate quite nicely some of the points we have been discussing previously. Before the violent outburst there is frustration and anger, and, as other parts of the interviews indicated, sometimes quite distinct paranoia: for example, the second motorist went on to say, 'I mean, it's blokes like him that should be picked up, the ones that cause all the trouble'. The degree to which full brain function is necessary to reduce this type of violent outburst is perhaps illustrated by the close association that has been found again and again in different countries of the world between alcohol and road accidents, and the dramatic fall in road accidents that occurred in Britain after the introduction of the breathalyser test.[174]

In his study Parry was able to pick out, by his very specific questionnaire asking about aggressive behaviour on the roads, people who were likely to have been involved in a serious crash, but he was also impressed by the non-aggressiveness they sometimes showed in other areas of their lives. He tended to think that people drive as they would like to live and quoted a young bank clerk who confessed to getting a thrill out of pretending that the North Circular Road in London was a motor-racing circuit; he had always wanted to be a motor racing driver. Numerous penalties for speeding and dangerous driving were all a big joke to him, yet he was an intelligent sensitive man who felt strongly about the misuse of atomic energy. As Parry puts it: 'People who would be willing to support charities, scorn the growth of social violence, uphold the law in other respects, and generally try to live as good citizens, change into selfish, aggressive, and dangerous beings in the time it takes to get into and start a car'.

It is probably because violence by car is so normal in the statistical sense that, on the whole, we do not condemn it. Motoring violence has almost become a sanctioned form of violence—'There but for fortune go you and I'—and as a public we are liable to indulge in criticisms of the police for checking our motoring indiscretions, exclaiming: 'Why don't they get on with looking for *real* criminals?' What is a criminal?

Parry found that of his 382 randomly selected male motorists, 9 per cent admitted to having been in a fight with other drivers, 13 per cent had tried to edge other cars off the road on occasions, 15 per cent had had murderous feelings to other drivers, and the whole group admitted to some 234 accidents, 51 of which were 'serious'. The younger motorist was most aggressive and most liable to accidents, and the lower middle classes produced a higher accident rate than other social groups.

The main differences between motoring violence and other forms of violence, it seems to me, are to be found in the physical characteristics of the car itself. As Whitlock[151] has suggested, in some respects it can be regarded as a transportable house or territory, and trespass into its path or surrounding space has to be countered as strenuously as is necessary for more permanent territories; but, perhaps even more important, it cuts the contestants off from one another, with the consequence that they cannot invoke an inhibitory mechanism before violence occurs—in particular, they cannot speak to one another. In respect of this latter point it is interesting to note that Parry[173] found that 83 per cent of men and 73 per cent of women drivers admitted to swearing under their breath at other drivers. Finally, of course, when aggression gets to the point of violence, the car takes on its other role of a dangerous weapon. Man was born with few natural weapons and is, therefore, unused to handling them; this one, which he has recently devised for himself, he sits inside and psychologically regards as an extension of himself.

Homicide

Violent motoring leads straight on to homicide in its various forms, and I am going to begin with homicide by car, because of the point made immediately above that motoring violence illustrates the general principles of criminal violence and because Table 1 shows that Causing Death by Dangerous Driving is in Britain numerically the most serious form of criminal homicide and is on the increase. As MacDonald[175] pointed out, not only is death by car a relatively effective way of killing or being killed, but it also offers special opportunities of concealment. He found that patients at a mental hospital had a fatal accident rate some thirty times greater than that of the general population and many of them died in circumstances suggestive of suicide, while other patients in the hospital confessed to both suicidal and homicidal attempts by automobile.

One of the factors which led me to suggest above that road violence is almost sanctioned is the surprising lack of concern society shows with regard to it compared with other forms of violence. Perhaps I can illustrate this by a recent quotation from the British press: 'A girl walking along a road, with two friends, was killed when a lorry driver drove his vehicle at them "to give them a fright", Shropshire Assizes was told yesterday. Two girls jumped clear... but the third ... aged 16... was hit and died from a fractured skull... (the driver)... pleaded guilty to causing death by dangerous driving. He was gaoled for nine months and banned from driving for five years'. This may well have been a very appropriate court decision in view of all the circumstances, but imagine the difference in concern and outcome there would have been if he had killed the girl with a different weapon.

Turning to murder in the full legal sense we could, of course, devote a whole book to this one subject alone. It fascinates, it horrifies. Countless thrillers involve a good juicy murder. It attracts massive publicity and yet, statistically, as we can see from Table 1, it is by no means the most important form of homicide. This may not be quite the case in America, but even there the murder rate has fallen since the 1930s, and is now only about 5/100,000 population/year; and murder, aggravated assault, rape and robbery added together only account for 13 per cent of all serious crime in the United States.[170]

It is important to realise that murder rates vary very widely from country to country, and from situation to situation. The rate for the United States is made up of widely varying rates between different states in the US, and there are social relationships within these figures that are very significant. Wolfgang[153] found, for example, that in Philadelphia 73 per cent of murder victims were negro and 75 per cent of offenders were negro, whereas at the time of his study they only comprised 18 per cent of the Philadelphia population. He also found the expected relation between males and homicide. In Britain the number of murders (including diminished responsibility manslaughters) known to the police varied during the years 1957-68 between 3.2 and 4.4 per million per year.[137]

The murder rate in Britain is surprisingly stable (there has been almost no variation in the rate since the 1930s[176]) compared with a soaring increase in the number of violence offences other than murder reported to the police. In view of the fact that chance takes a hand when someone dangerously assaults another person (eg, fitness of the victim, position of the blow or bullet), two possible explanations seem to account for this. Either, as I suggested earlier, murders have always been mostly reported to the police and the recent increase in violence figures is related not to an underlying increase in violent crime but to an increase in the report rate, or modern medicine is saving a lot of lives that would previously have been lost. Most probably, both these things are happening simultaneously.

A third fundamental is murder's special association with mental illness. In Britain the proportion of murder suspects who commit suicide varies between 15 and 33 per cent, a substantial proportion by any reckoning; a further 28-40 per cent are deemed abnormal in court by reason of insanity or diminished responsibility, which only leaves 33-47 per cent of murderers who can be regarded as normal in the legal sense. Dr Donald West[135] studied some seventy-eight murder/ suicide incidents that occurred in the London Metropolitan Police District and the Home Counties between 1954 and 1961. All but one of the murderers killed themselves before arrest. In this sample the popular stereotype of the murderer

as a confirmed criminal who kills for gain was hardly repre-
sented at all; it showed, in fact, a heavy preponderance of
domestic killings of wife, child or lover. West emphasised that
in Britain murders followed by suicide constitute numerically
so substantial a section of the murder statistics that their
special characteristics profoundly affect any criminological
analysis of murder. 'Commonly accepted generalisations such
as the assumption that nearly all murders are committed by
men, that most insane murderers are schizophrenics, or that
the lower classes predominate among offenders, hold true
only so long as the crimes followed by suicide are resolutely
disregarded.' He also concluded that the intimate connection
between self-destructive and aggressive tendencies emerged
clearly.

Perhaps the most important fundamental for the newcomer to this field to grasp, which has already been stated
but needs emphasis, is that murder is more often than not a
family or a domestic matter. This is true on both sides of the
Atlantic. In Wolfgang's Philadelphia study[153] close friendships
and family relationships accounted for more than half the
murderous interactions, and only 12 per cent of victims were
strangers, 1 per cent police officers, and 1 per cent innocent
bystanders. Similar findings hold for Britain,[137] where it has
also been shown that murders of women and children were
mainly due to rage, quarrels or jealousy, whilst for men, rage,
quarrels, jealousy and revenge accounted for about half the
known motives.

Needless to add, the factors we have considered previously
all play their part in the ultimate form of intra-human violence. Special attention should perhaps be directed to alcohol,
which, presumably by interfering with self-control, seems to
be commonly associated with murder. [153, 177, 178] Training would
seem to be of little relevance to the type of emotional outburst I have suggested as a common basis of murder, and yet
we must never forget that when a deadly violent situation
arises people who have been trained to kill are going to have

a number of appropriate skills ready to hand. There is evidence, for example, that a number of adult killers may have been brutalised as children (p65).

Any reader unfamiliar with the types of crime that murder comprises should not turn to thrillers, crime novelists and the like but instead read *A Calendar of Murder* by Morris and Blom-Cooper.[179] It is an excellent compendium of thumbnail sketches of all the 764 men and women who were tried for murder in England and Wales between 21 March 1957 and 3 December 1962.

The killing of children is a specially emotive topic, stirring condemnation and horror to maximum levels at times, and yet, paradoxically, one form of child murder—infanticide—has produced, in Britain at least, the most liberal and compassionate legal arrangement of any form of homicide. As Walker[139] puts it in his discussion of its history: 'It provides a special defence which succeeds in glossing over the issue of responsibility, and it confines this defence to women'. The paradox is all the greater because this attitude has not been universal. In the Middle Ages it was specially condemned and the murdering mother was treated with special severity. However, by the nineteenth century such women were usually reprieved. Since 1923 the proportion of women found guilty of killing their own babies aged less than one year who have been imprisoned has fallen from 49 per cent to 1 per cent.[139] This is a very remarkable legal phenomenon, which has, in part, been brought about by an increasing tolerance of behaviour that instinctively, empathically, we regard as 'mad'.[180] Perhaps also, as Walker has suggested, it has been helped by legally sidestepping the word 'murder', which carries emotional overtones out of all proportion to its legal and criminological significance.

Battered Baby Syndrome

It is a remarkable fact that it was not until 1946[181] that doctors began to realise that babies brought to them by their parents with mysterious injuries putatively associated with minor accidents were, in fact, not suffering from 'fragile bones' but were the victims of enraged assaults by their emotionally disturbed mothers or fathers. Since then the problem has become increasingly recognised and the reported figures have leapt up (perhaps a good example of decreasing public acquiescence producing increasing violence figures).

Kempe and his colleagues[182] wrote one of the earliest extensive reports on this subject, and they noticed a great variability in the type of person who offended in this way, although they accepted that the majority fall into the unsatisfactory 'sociopathic' or 'psychopathic' category described earlier (p114), with alcoholism (p118), sexual promiscuity, unstable marriages, and other criminal activities being re portedly common. Their experience also taught them that the attacking of children was not confined to people with a psychopathic personality or of borderline socio-economic status; it occurs also among people with good education and a stable financial background. Harking back to earlier comments on brutalisation during childhood (p65 and p69), it is interesting that these authors note there is also some suggestion that the attacking parent was subjected to similar abuse in childhood. It would appear that one of the most important factors to be found in families where parental assault occurs is 'to do unto others as you have been done by....!' Two English surveys confirm these American findings about the type of parent who attacks his (or her) child.[183, 184]

One of the most worrying findings reported by the British NSPCC study[184] was the persistence of the problem. In their study of seventy-eight battered children under the age of four, two out of every five children had previously been injured to an extent sufficient to warrant medical attention. Three out of every five who were discharged home after hospital treatment had to be readmitted because of subsequent injury. The NSPCC workers divided the parents they saw into two groups. First was the habitually aggressive group who comprised 47 per cent of their sample; most of these had criminal records, were prone to violent outbursts of temper, had stormy personal relationships (cf, psychopaths). A second group were the 'emotionally impoverished', who either expected the baby to do all the giving of affection, like the 18-year-old single girl who could not tolerate the baby when he cried in a demanding way, or who became distraught by babyish behaviour alien to the rigid structure they had established for themselves, like the 20-year-old mother who kept her home in immaculate order and was revolted by her baby's untidy eating.

Rape

There is often an element of aggression involved in a sexual offence, but the one sexual crime that can be really violent is rape. It is probably best defined as sexual intercourse between a man and a woman of any age, who are not married, by means of force, fraud, or intimidation. Like other violent offences the figures for rape are on the increase (see Table 1). As with other violent crimes, however, it is difficult to know how to interpret these figures, especially as the police clear-up rate is low. Transatlantic comparisons are also difficult because in America the law is slightly different and sexual intercourse with a girl under the age of legal consent, even if she is very compliant or even enticing, is statutory rape, and the age of legal consent varies from 7 years in Delaware to 21 years in Tennessee!

Normal sexual behaviour has elements of aggression in it —the love bite, the woman who asks her man not to be too gentle, advertisements that depict 'helpless' damsels being swept off their feet. In one sense, therefore, forcible rape can be seen as the extension of a normal process; indeed it is clear that some 'rapes' are the result of a misunderstanding between courting partners—she entices and encourages him, he thinks her protestations that they have 'gone far enough' are either part of the game or a deference to social convention and he is thereby encouraged to firmer methods. A considerable number of rape charges are also quite simply false, made by women either as an attempt to destroy a former lover or as a means of preserving a moral image when caught out; as Kinsey has said, 'the difference between a good time and a rape may hinge on whether the girl's parents were awake when she finally arrived home'.[185] Nevertheless, the brutal sadistic rape, sometimes carried out by one individual, sometimes by a group, does happen, and it can even be followed or accompanied by murder.

In a recent book describing many cases of rape, together with its legal ramifications, MacDonald[186] suggests that sadistic rape is not merely an extension of normal sexual behaviour. In fact, most offenders could obtain their sexual satisfactions at less cost, and quite a lot of them are married anyway. One case he describes is of a man who one afternoon broke into a house to rape a young married woman. He was wearing a stocking mask on his face and he forced her to undress at gunpoint; when she tried to run away in the nude he shot her in the leg. Following this he drove to a beauty parlour and forced the three women in it into the back room, made them undress and raped one of them. From his own account, the offender had a disturbed relationship with his mother; she was over-protective and tried to feminise him. His father died when he was five and sometimes he feels guilty about this. A stepfather died soon after, but a second stepfather was cruel and used to whip him, and even threatened members of the family with a gun. At the age of thirteen his mother told him he was adopted, whereupon he tried to kill himself. 'I thought my real mother was a prostitute who hadn't taken precautions.' MacDonald emphasises in his book that he believes the rapist is often not just desperate for love or sex, but hostile to women, and frequently this stems from hostility to a significant woman in his childhood.

In the example quoted it is also worth noting that the rapist had committed almost 200 criminal offences including burglary, armed robbery, indecent liberties, previous rapes and attempted rapes, theft, indecent exposure and destruction by fire. Gebhard and his colleagues[185] studied 140 sexual aggressors in San Quentin gaol and gained the impression that the majority could be described as 'criminally inclined men who take what they want, whether money, material or women, and their sex offences are byproducts of their general criminality'. They noted the offenders' sexual adjustment in terms of marriages, girl friends and the like to be 'quantitatively well above average', and there were only occasional hints of underlying violence and sadism, but 'in the sex offence itself, however, one can frequently see a basic pathology revealed by unnecessary violence, bizarre behaviour and self-delusion'.

Group rape is an even more horrifying phenomenon and perhaps even harder to account for because it has to be seen in social terms and cannot be understood simply in terms of personal pathology. MacDonald suggests that it is not uncommon (16 per cent of the rapes in Denmark, 50 per cent of those in Toronto, 66 per cent of those in Finland), and is a special problem among younger and teenage males. Certainly it can occur as a kind of teenage gang ritual, the girl chosen being either someone with a reputation for promiscuity or someone who is joining or has joined the group anyway.

Robbery

As already indicated, the British criminal statistics classify this offence under property offences, not violent offences. This is because it is theft by the use or *threat* of force. Nevertheless, some robberies can be very violent indeed and most members of the public think of it as a violent crime. Unlike murder, robbery has increased considerably in England and Wales in recent years from 1,039 convictions in 1960 to 2,123 in 1968. There has also been a similar increase in recent years in the United States,[170] although the figures there are still something like 30 per cent below their 1933 peak.

As with murder, we are both repelled and attracted by robbery. Robbers tend to become heroes (Robin Hood, Dick Turpin), sometimes even within their own lifetime; in England recently there was a great deal of swashbuckling regard for the great train robbers. In prison robbers are not infrequently given a special kind of respect by less daring and perhaps less effective criminals.

The variety of cases that come under the heading of robbery is astonishing—anything from boys demanding sweets from other children by menaces to the member of the sophisticated wages sn..·h gang. McLintock and Gibson in their comprehensive study[187] describe five types: (1) robbery of people in charge of money and valuables, eg, the wages snatch, (2) sudden attacks on people in the open, (3) the housebreaker who is disturbed at his task, (4) robbery with a sexual connotation, eg, of a prostitute by a client, and (5) robbery of an associate or friend. Unlike other types of violence, robbery is usually committed among relative strangers, only 3.5 per cent of the offences falling into category (5). However, like other forms of violence, it is almost always carried out by males and usually against males. Threats only were used in 14-18 per cent of all the offences and in at least 7 per cent of all cases the injuries were so negligible that no treatment was required in hospital; but fractures and major wounds did occur in 10-12 per cent of offences, and bruises, etc, in 51-55 per cent.

One of the impressive characteristics of the effective professional criminal who is prepared to carry a weapon to gain money is his skill. I have talked to many of these men and they will freely describe their training; they do not call it that but most of them have come through a well established school. As youngsters they learn to steal, either from delinquent elders or as a means of striking back at an intolerable environment. They are constantly in trouble, being regarded at first as 'behaviour disordered' or 'delinquent', but later labelled as 'criminals' and 'sent away' either to an approved school or to a Borstal. Having been given the criminal role and thrust out from ordinary society they accept their lot, join the club, and learn the trade. As with any active group, friendships are formed, introductions made, and opportunities offered. These opportunities can include big money, and the sanctions of society have little or no chance against the rewards of friendship plus money, especially when the clear-up rate is so low and any one man may have been involved in a dozen or more robberies before his first robbery conviction.

Is it reasonable to regard robbers as different from other types of violent offender? Apart from the overlap area (McLintock and Gibson's 25 per cent of violent character) I think it is. In the main they use their violence in a controlled calculated way rather like a soldier, and in many respects they are trained to violent standards. Robert Allerton's descriptions of himself express this point as well as anybody in the current literature, and I will quote one or two telling phrases from his book: [188]

> Stall-holders would give a couple of kids ½d each to have a fight.
> If somebody sloshed you, you sloshed him. It was as much part of everyday life and behaviour as the houses, was violence.
> The other thing that was normal as well as violence was people going to prison.
> Violence is in a way like bad language... I don't at all recoil from the idea, I don't have a sort of inborn dislike of the thing, like you do. As long as I can remember, I've seen violence in me, all around me.
> If I can see a chance of earning myself—or making myself, if you prefer it—a few thousand quid all at one go, naturally I'll do it. It's only what people, millions of them, are trying to do on the football pools every week.
> So violence is wrong, on a fundamental level, I admit that. But on a day to day level it just happens that it's a tool of my trade and I use it—like an engineer uses a slide rule, or a bus driver the handbrake, or a dentist the drill. Only when necessary, and only when it can't be avoided. If I've got to whack a bloke with an iron bar to make him let go of a wages bag he's carrying, O.K.

So I'll whack him. If he lets go without any trouble, I don't.
That's all.

Violent Criminals

Robert Allerton's self-portrait leads us to consider 'the violent
criminal' as an entity. Such a concept is of limited help,
because people appearing in court are such a heterogeneous
group that to try and sort them into violent and non-violent
categories is relatively meaningless. As we have seen, it is
possible for a man who appears non-violent in most of his
activities to become a dangerous menace on the roads. Equally
a 'murderer' may be a meek and mild individual who has
had one devastatingly violent outburst under severe provocation. Furthermore, men who are frequently in fights at the
age of twenty may be relatively pacific at the age of forty.
Nevertheless, we are still apt to think of some people as
specially violent. I suppose we mean that people like Robert
Allerton are frequently in trouble with the law because of
violence; they are either prepared to fight idiosyncratically
with all the means at their disposal against the established
order and rules, in the same way that a large group may fight
to gain control or defend itself, or they are petulant and explosive in temperament so that minor provocation results in
violence, or they are under such severe stress and frustration
that the only reasonable 'normal' response is attack. Here,
however, we have three groups, and I believe that it is a mistake to try and understand criminal violence without taking
into account training and previous experience of violence,
temperament and the degree of external frustration and stress
suffered. In this framework we can see why the concept of
'the violent man' will not work, because, once again, we are
forced back to our interaction model. Violence is not just
dependent upon the individual, it is also dependent upon the
environment he finds himself in. In other words, we can
describe whether or not a particular individual has been
violent in the past, and in what situations, but this is not

entirely predictive of the future because we cannot foretell what situations he will find himself in then.

An attempt to classify violence in terms of both the individual and the environmental factors has been made by Megargee,[189] who has postulated a dimension of overcontrol/undercontrol of violence. He noted the 'meek and mild' type of murderer who resides in prison along with the Robert Allertons of the world and suggested that they both have control disabilities. The first man is usually overcontrolled, with rigid inhibitions against overt aggressive behaviour, but with mounting provocation the tension builds up and up until there is an eruption of devastating proportions. The second type is, however, chronically undercontrolled, so that he is always firing off with assaultative outbursts to even slight frustrations. Presumably this hypothesis means that those of us who do not get into trouble are either endowed with normal (non-pathological) levels of aggression control or are overcontrolled but never stressed enough to have an outburst. Megargee has tried to test his theory by looking at the results of personality tests carried out on people who have been violent. As he himself admits, there is no really strong support for his views and other workers[190] have not been able to find the expected clear dichotomy.

Recently some colleagues and I[191] have examined a number of prisoners and Borstal lads to see if we could fit them on to a violence scale and to see if the sub-dimensions of frequency of violence and destructiveness in the violence were separate aspects. While we found we could rank the offenders quite reliably along a violence gradient, we were unhappy about the validity of such a process because of the variety of people lumped together ostensibly in the same category. The frequency and destructiveness scales gave a better descriptive framework when used together, but the scales were, in fact, closely related to one another, which suggested that, at least on the pragmatic descriptive level, Megargee's two distinct groups seem unlikely. In describing his two groups Megargee seems to be implying that some people are very destructive *because* they are only infrequently aggressive. It is probably better to remove the 'because' and describe each man on the three-dimensional framework of frequency/location/destructiveness. How often is he violent, in what circumstances (ie, under what particular stresses and strains), and how destructive does he get when he is violent?

Once more we are reminded that 'crime', or any subcategory of crime such as violence, is an unsatisfactory basis for a human classification system because ultimately it is socially determined and defined and classifications that have biological meaning must take their standpoint from biological (including, of course, psychological) criteria. Charlotte Banks[192] reminds us:

> It is not only the keeper .... who may come to see criminals as a homogeneous, amorphous mass of guilt. Such a habit of thought seems to pervade popular notions .... An implicit assumption underlying such thought is that offenders are a group apart from other people. And this is an assumption that can lead directly to two unfortunate consequences. First it may lead us to affix the label 'criminal' a little too easily. Once a boy has been convicted of an offence ... he often ceases to be for us an ordinary person ... he becomes ... an object of contumely, of false sentiment, of unrealistic theories ... Secondly, having affixed a label ... we are tempted to hunt feverishly for a few simple 'variables' which we think ought to distinguish between 'criminals' and the rest; hoping against hope that offenders and their offences, *en masse*, can be explained by a few broad strokes on a canvas, a fiendish, modern action painting perhaps—membership of a sub-culture; social and emotional immaturity; lack of super-ego; intolerance of frustration or, more popularly speaking, thuggery, hooliganism, teddy-boy morals and so on.

References to this chapter appear on pp189-90

9 *Methods of Control*

Before we can even consider the question of controlling violence, we have to consider a fundamental issue. By control do we mean a reduction in the total amount of violence or simply a shift of violence from the area we do not sanction to the area we do? To some extent this issue is related to long-term and short-term objectives. For example, it may be expedient, even 'necessary' in political terms, to respond to a riot by counter violence. An even bigger show of violence, a quasi-military police force may for some time be able to contain a potentially violent situation, but in the long run these measures are unlikely to reduce the totality of violence simply because they use violence. If we are serious in seeking control of violence, we have to aim for a reduction in the amount and we have to break the vicious circle of first one side and then the other trying to solve a conflict violently. Armed occupation to control guerrilla action or the elimination of violent criminals by killing them may seem to reduce violence in the short run, but by demonstrating that violence works, by increasing frustrations, by not seeking for causes, it may well increase violence in the long run.

If, then, we mean by control the long-term reduction of violence, how much reduction do we want? Previous chapters have shown that violence has biological and social functions.

important to our evolution. Its total elimination, therefore, will leave a hiatus and unless that can be filled by an equally powerful evolutionary force, it is possible that man will be worse not better off. Perhaps all we need to do is to ensure that, while violence may continue, destructiveness does not get out of hand so that we can avoid the ultimate cataclysm? This maybe could be achieved by weapons control, so that nuclear, biological and other such total weapons are ruled out. That is the only solution we require for the survival of our species. Man is an emotional creature, however, and values personal survival as well as group survival, and a reduction of human suffering is one of his collateral aims.

There are one or two encouraging signs that evolution towards non-violence is possible. Any such evolutionary process is bound to seem interminably slow to an individual observer, but man has only existed for some 500,000 years, and if he were to evolve a non-violent civilisation within the next 500,000 that would be an incredible achievement. Remember the ant took 50 million years to produce its complicated but violent social system. At one level periods of time of this order seem ridiculous, because in the interim man may well blow himself up or pollute himself to death. But the central point is contained in our very concern about this issue—man may be intelligent enough and powerful enough not only to reflect and introspect, but also to take avoiding action. The impact of a nuclear explosion may be as important an evolutionary factor on man's consciousness as the nuclear fallout is on his genes. Furthermore, although at times *homosapiens* may be careless of individual lives, he has a very powerful urge towards the preservation of the group. Before a nuclear or biological war could begin, two or more large groups would either have to over-ride this urge or completely misunderstand the consequences.

General Principles

We have seen that violence cannot be seen as a single entity, for there are different types of violence, and even more clearly there is no single cause behind it. Methods of control will, therefore, have to be various. Panaceas, nostrums and homilies are all unlikely to be successful. Even so a system of general principles of violence control can probably be postulated.

Firstly, with any social phenomenon, control is enhanced by the understanding of its cause. Broadly, in this volume I have tried to look at three different determinants of violence: (1) weaponry and destructiveness, (2) precipitants, and (3) human attitudes. I believe that violence control is best examined for each of these determinants. Other distinctions I have made in the book have been between individual and group violence (with international violence as a special subsection of group violence), between sanctioned and unsanctioned violence and between healthy violence and sick violence; these aspects need to be taken into consideration in each of the three main areas.

Of the three determinants, *attitudes* is by far the most important because, basically, it is man's view of himself, his inner aggressive needs, his relationship with his fellow man that finally determines whether violence occurs or not. If violent attitudes were to disappear altogether, then precipitants could not trigger a fight and weapons would lie idle. However, as I have already emphasised, at that point *homo sapiens* would have made a fundamental change, he may even warrant a new name, *homo pacificus*. That is too far away to contemplate, but in the meantime, surely we can change human attitudes slightly—our children's attitudes about violence, for example? Fortunately, we have almost no power to manipulate the psychology of man in a coherent pre-selected way—I say fortunately, for such power could become the ultimate form of aggression—but undoubtedly, as we have already seen, many attitudes are the result of education and a previous cultural inheritance. There may be marginal and in the end crucial ways in which we can direct this learning process away from violence.

One of the major objectives in seeking for control of violence is the establishment of a stable hierarchy. Some of the animal studies may have led us to believe that hierarchies only work through physical strength and the threat of violence. This is only partly true in man, who has a number of emotional and dependency needs which, if unfulfilled, leave him in a precarious position, and so those who can fulfil such needs have power over the individual concerned. In a well organised family, for example, the children obey their parents because they need approval, affection and such like, all of which can be withheld for disobedience. Nevertheless, father also gains some of his respect by his size, his strength, his earning capacity, his ability to manipulate the technology of his time to bring power and protection to his family. In a modern western family when violence (corporal punishment, assaults, brutality) is used to maintain the family hierarchy, this is often because of a failure of the more subtle measures and frequently indicates that the hierarchy is crumbling.

In the wider community similar patterns can be discerned. People usually respect their leaders for their skills and abilities and for fulfilling needs right throughout the hierarchy. If needs are not fulfilled at the lower end of a hierarchy, that hierarchy can still be maintained by means of aggression backed by violence. Ultimately, however, sub-groupings will form with sub-leaders who do obtain their power without violence, so that polarised groupings and violence between the various factions becomes an increased possibility. Perhaps the events of Northern Ireland are a good illustration of this mechanism.

It may also be necessary for a stable hierarchy to develop among groups if inter-group violence is to be avoided. South-wick's observations of rhesus monkeys (p24) clearly indicated that a rank order among groups can develop. In this context it is perhaps significant that no stable hierarchy exists in international affairs. Nations are constantly jostling for supremacy and no central system or group has yet been satisfactorily formed to which everybody can give unequivocal allegiance. Perhaps the establishment of super-powers and satellites is an early attempt to solve this problem.

Weapons Control

Throughout it has been emphasised that if man did not have artificial weapons, his violence would be of minor significance; it would certainly be used to establish hierarchies and dominance but the death-rate would be low and we would certainly not be anxiously wondering about total annihilation and discussing violence control. Equally, if man did not have weapons, he would not be *homo sapiens*, since his brainpower has brought him knowledge and technology, which he presses into service whenever he has a problem to solve, and violence is no exception.

In a well organised group the leaders can increase their power by ensuring that most of the really lethal weapons are in their hands, well under control. By this means the power structure cannot be threatened by superiority of weapons among dissidents, and, of course, the weapons themselves need not be used, simply because they do not have to counter equal weapons. Most nations try to arrange that the powerful weapons, such as firearms, are only permitted to selected individuals. The more efficient the nation is in this regard, the lower will be its death-rate from unsanctioned violence. This is illustrated in Table 3.

Table 3   Deaths due to firearms in rates per 100,000 population

Country	Homicide	Suicide	Accident	Laws
USA (1966)	3.5	5.3	1.3	Lax
Canada (1966)	0.5	3.1	1.0	Gun registration
Sweden (1966)	0.2	2.5	0.3	" "
France (1965)	0.3	1.8	0.5	Police permits
German Fed Rep (1965)	0.1	0.9	0.2	Hunters only
Scotland (1963)	0.1	0.4	0.3	Police permits
Eng & Wales (1966)	0.1	0.4	0.1	" "
Japan (1965)	0.1	0.1	0.1	Prohibition

(These figures are quoted from Gillin and Ochberg[107])

The difference between the top of the table and bottom—19,820 deaths due to firearms in America in 1966 and 162 in Japan in 1965—is very striking, and the close relationship with the type of legislation in force is obvious. An interesting aspect of the British figures is that the police are unarmed, and senior police officials, criminologists and criminals alike all agree that this is an important factor in the low level of gun-carrying in violent crimes in Britain. The robber does not feel that he needs to defend himself against an armed policeman. Of the 9,379 robberies in England and Wales in 1967 and 1968 only 6.8 per cent (637) involved firearms, and in those two years there were only thirteen victims of serious injury and thirty-five of slight injury during robberies, about 8 per cent of all firearm robberies.[193]

This is not the place to debate all the issues involved in the American gun-law controversy (see Daniels et al[106] for a good account), but we can surely predict with some confidence that were the United States government to introduce strict and enforced legislation preventing the widespread ownership of firearms in that country, the deathrate due to firearms would fall. Those who are against gun laws will argue that the deathrate would not alter because other weapons would be chosen. 'It's not the gun which kills, it's the man who pulls the trigger.' There is some truth in this, since the man who is having a frenzied row with his wife may reach for a knife if no gun is available, but it should be remembered that knives are more revolting to use and they are not so lethal wound for wound; furthermore, the knife used would have virtually to be a dagger, not necessarily a household object in the same way that a gun is in some parts of America. On the other hand, proponents of gun laws like myself must never forget that ultimately the need for weapons is an attitudinal problem stemming from fear. The level of hostility to gun laws is only partly based on economics. It is also related to group anxieties about criminals, communists, lunatics and the like. Reduce the fear, change the attitudes, and the gun laws will follow.

As far as domestic and criminal violence is concerned we cannot, of course, concentrate exclusively upon the gun. Perhaps the most important weapon of all in this regard is the one that is never considered a weapon—the automobile. Consideration is given in most countries to the skill and competence of a driver, but as yet we have been unable to devise ways of preventing a vehicle being misused for violence.

In the international sphere fear is again the biggest driving force in persuading nations to keep large stocks of arms. One of the most remarkable changes in international politics this century has been the decline of the expansionist policy. War has perhaps already begun to outlive its usefulness, for it is now rarely thought that the best road to international power and influence is by armed invasion; but the fear that others may still believe in this method dies much harder. Even fear has its uses, though, and it is almost certainly fear of annihilation that has led to discussions about nuclear and biological arms control. During World War II it was possible to produce some arms limitation by mutual fear, which was no doubt the reason that poison gases were not used. At the moment only a few highly privileged countries have weapons of ultimate destructiveness, and these nations have tacit and uneasy agreements that such weapons will not be used. Other nations cannot challenge these 'super-powers' by violence, but have to find more subtle measures. Perhaps we are groping our way towards a stable hierarchy of nations, though we know from our experience of lower-order hierarchies that such a hierarchy will only be really stable and insusceptible to violence when the dominant groups genuinely obtain their authority from the non-dominant groups, where power is not itself enforced by violence and when the hierarchy has clear mechanisms for fulfilling the needs of all its member groups.

Reduction of Precipitants
The factors we have previously considered as precipitants of violence are frustrations, grievances and pain, unstable social

systems and hierarchies, and crowding and a shortage of resources. Glibly, then, we can prescribe that these factors be removed or reduced. In practice, attitudes have to change before this can happen. The National Advisory Commission on Civil Disorders[122] recommended a number of concrete ways in which the frustrations and grievances behind American inter-racial strife could be reduced: neighbourhood action task forces, a reorganisation of local government so that it could be more in touch with local needs, better police protection for ghetto residents, fair and effective means of dealing with grievances against the police, and a recruitment drive for negroes to join the police force. The extent to which these measures are being tried and are operational is directly dependent upon attitudes towards 'the others', the fear of being attacked, and the genuineness of the desire for non-violence that is felt by both the individuals in authority and ordinary citizens.

Assuming that the point can be achieved where everybody is concerned to reduce violence, what specific acts appear as useful experiments in the light of what we have seen so far? In the international field the population explosion in some parts of the world clearly needs curtailing, presumably by massive contraception programmes; food distribution needs to be streamlined and equalised so that the obscenity of one section of the world's community becoming malnourished by reason of obesity while others starve is removed; and resources in general need to be more equally shared so that the ever-widening and, therefore, potentially explosive gap between the rich and the poor nations is narrowed. The greatest danger to mankind, however, is the violence potential of the so-called super-powers. Here it is essential that frustrations between them are kept to a minimum, that each respects the needs of all the others, and that systems are developed to resolve tensions and frustration before armed conflict is resorted to. Diplomatic channels are clearly at a premium in this kind of activity, and a great deal of historical and operational research is required to find out which methods are successful and which are not, which research needs to be carried out in real, human, international situations. In addition, an international forum is required. This century has provided two—first, the League of Nations and now the United Nations. In spite of failures and limitations the international forum may be the most important war-prevention factor man has yet devised.

Even when attitudes are not really ready for violence substitutes, there may still be mechanisms that will operate. The fascinating robber's cave experiment designed by Sherif and his colleagues[194] demonstrated very neatly something we tend to assume anyway, that conflict between two groups can be resolved by the appearance of an external common enemy. It is, for example, not unknown for an insecure national leader to divert attention from internal dissension by pointing an accusing finger at outsiders. Perhaps this was part of the explanation for Nazi expansionism.

Sherif took two groups of 11-year-old middle-class Protestant American boys, well adjusted but all strangers to each other, and divided them into two groups. Initially there were twenty-two boys but two went home because of homesickness. The first discovery the researchers made was that cultural, physical, and economic differences were not necessary for conflict, nor were neurotic or unstable personality tendencies. All that was required was two groups competing for one goal. A series of competitive games was arranged between the two groups— baseball, tug of war, football, tent-pitching, and a treasure hunt. Very quickly hostility arose between them, and then various methods of reducing the ill-will were tried. First, contact methods were used, both groups eating together, going to the cinema together, picnicking together, shooting firecrackers together, but none of these methods produced a reduction in hostility. Then a superordinate goal scheme was introduced. The water supply to their mutual camp was drastically curtailed, and they were told that volunteers were needed to help locate the fault. Members of both groups volunteered. After the tank had been found to be three-quarters full and the fault to be a sack stuffed in the outlet pipe, joint participation succeeded in removing the blockage. After the event there was courtesy in allowing the thirstier boys to drink first and some intermingling of the groups. By the evening, however, the groups were insulting one another again. The next superordinate goal was the securing of a movie, but the groups were left to find the $15 among themselves; eventually an equitable solution between the groups was reached. After a further series of such problems, group hostility was reduced to the point where they virtually became one group.

A number of interesting points are raised by this work. This may well operate, as in the experiment, on a sub-group level, but can it work between, say, the USSR and the USA? Obviously external human scapegoats are useless—both countries united against Germany in 1941 and they could conceivably unite against China now, but no reduction in violence results, as man is still attacking man. But in the experiment with the boys the environment, man's old and common enemy, was utilised. Why not in international affairs? The conquest of space is a possibility, but this is limited to two countries, is not action against an enemy, and in any case, a competitive space *race*, which could conceivably inflame ill-feeling between the two nations, has already developed. Pollution seems a more likely area for cooperation, for it now affects all countries of the world. Without international agreement and action the whole human race could be destroyed, and collaboration is urgent and vital; if it comes, it could provide the framework for nations to unite as one group in the common struggle for survival.

At the civil strife level surely no one can suggest better methods of reducing precipitants than those already quoted from the President's National Advisory Commission. The basic elements are a more equitable distribution of resources, a power structure that takes its authority from the hierarchy it dominates (ie, people are voluntarily ruled), and mechanisms for resolution of conflict by non-violent means such as discussion.

At the criminal level (murder, violent assaults, battered babies, robbery, rape and the like) the precipitants are very personal and outside of general social control, but a few general factors do probably operate. Robbery, for example, is best seen as an extension of theft, and the factors underlying stealing such as those discussed by Merton (p76) need to be corrected; we have got to find some way of adapting our competitive goal-orientated society so that large segments do not feel that all the targets established are unattainable by legitimate means. Equally we have to provide sufficient space, or territory, for everybody, so that irritable husbands, wives and children do not jar one another's nerves by constant proximity. Two important precipitants of violent crime we have not considered at all so far are loneliness and homelessness. Both may lead to or be associated with excessive drinking, and both produce intense frustration and anger. In recent months I have known two lonely frustrated men to be violent in various ways. The first felt rejected by society, found it increasingly difficult to obtain work, fell out with his girl friend and lost his lodgings; he was an alcoholic and he killed himself, but not before he had made some homicidal threats which he could well have carried out, since he had often been violent in the past. The second is incapable of surviving outside an institution, but in spite of not being mad or 'ill' in the formal sense he has spent a good deal of his life in mental hospitals. When his local hospital finally rejected him, he became desperate because of his homelessness and decided to prove his madness and need for a mental hospital bed by starting a number of serious fires; one of these nearly caused a death.

Alteration of Attitudes
Attitudes, drives, desires, call them what you will, are the basis of all aggressive activities, including violence. Even when a man is simply being violent because he is told to do so, he

obeys because of his attitude of cooperativeness; his superior has had the violent desire. Change attitudes, therefore, and all the rest follows. Not so easy, but our review has told us to start in childhood. Training is the key to this problem, although unfortunately we are, as yet, all too ignorant about the consequences of any changes we may make. When we considered the question of film and TV violence, for example, there were opposing views about the effects of different kinds of programme, and we are not yet in a position to be sure which is the correct one.

For the average child we as a community have to make up our minds that we are concerned about violence training. Then we have to give one another, and especially our children, non-violent examples of behaviour to copy. Violence of all kinds should be eschewed (eg, corporal punishment to children) and violent acts should never be condoned or sanctioned. When people have violent feelings, the community must devise ways of indicating that acting upon these feelings is not acceptable, but it must do so in non-violent ways. For the children brought up in a disturbed environment we need courage to act on our knowledge that those who are persistently ill treated, beaten up, and brutalised are especially likely to become violent adults and should be removed to a loving and non-violent environment.

The effects of prejudice and hate must to some extent be minimised by legislation that gives an ostracised group the right to defend itself without resort to fighting. In other words, civil liberties should not just be a conceptual framework. Any aggrieved individual who feels persecuted by other individuals, or by the police, or by the state should have the opportunity to appeal to an independent third party as an arbitrator. The Race Relations Board is a tentative step in this direction in Great Britain, but as yet it is not sufficiently understood, or sufficiently independent of the white majority, to be the complete answer. Nevertheless, it is a beginning and could be extended with profit.

Diseased attitudes are fortunately not very common, or at least they do not lead to violence very commonly, but means of earlier detection and control could be developed with advantage. In particular, individuals who give warning of homicide or violent assault should be taken very seriously and given full medical facilities, just as we often do for the person who threatens suicide, and individuals who compulsively or persistently attack their children should, if only for the benefit of the next generation, be given intensive and long-term assistance.

International attitudes are slowly changing towards non-violence; increased communication and travel between nations will undoubtedly help to accelerate this progress. It is very difficult to think of Germans, or Russians, or Chinese, as pigs if you regularly go on holiday with them, or meet them at international conferences and develop friendships. Unsung bodies such as the United Nations Educational, Scientific & Cultural Organisation, the World Health Organisation, and the like, play an important role in fostering international communication.

Reduction of War Dangers

Total elimination of war is just not conceivable at this stage in history. It is sanctioned violence and, in some ways, it may even be desirable violence. My guess is that we are only considering a reduction in war because the species is in peril. That may be slightly too cynical. It is possible that the mass media, which, as I have already made clear, we do not unequivocally comprehend, may have brought us information and educated us to the point of disgust, so that enough people are revolted at the sights of real violence to form a group movement against it, but I suspect that the group survival motive is the stronger one.

Waskow[195] has suggested that there are two possible types of warless world: (1) one governed by a world government that has all the legal, executive and military powers vested in it, and (2) disarmed disorder in which every nation uses all forms of aggression except violence. Clearly nationalism is much too strong at present for a world government to seem anything other than a science-fiction phantasy, and the competitive rivalry between nations or interested groups within a world state could still bring about unsanctioned violence on a fairly large scale. The argument against disarmed disorder is obvious: aggression ultimately implies the threat of violence and sometimes the threat has to be enforced, at which point war breaks out. Waskow himself suggests that a lesser kind of world consensus, short of world government, may be achieved by setting up a world state which has all the military power invested in it and which would be called upon to settle disputes between nations. He does not explain, however, how one would prevent such a powerful state rapidly becoming a brutal dictatorship, engendering its own frustrations, and how an international police system would gain the respect and sanction of every single nation—a tall order.

Flugel[196] postulates three complementary approaches to the prevention of war. Firstly, a moral and religious approach in which individuals must be made to feel that they are their nation's keepers—an idea which, as Flugel admits, flies in the face of all we know about human psychology, since exhortations asking people to change their nature are singularly unsuccessful and obedience to the group is a powerful force. His second approach is to strengthen the United Nations by publicity, an anthem, and an international language. Thirdly, he sees the lessening of sexual restraints as producing less frustration, and the alleviation of economic hardship as reducing social tension, while he recommends that more international aggression should be expressed in substitute ways such as sport. This recommendation comes again and again from authors, perhaps most forcibly from Lorenz.[5] Perhaps at a general level sporting fixtures may foster international relations, as, for example, in the recent table-tennis diplomacy between the USA and China; but in a tense situation ritual-ised sporting contests can actually provoke rather than reduce feelings of hostility. The 1936 Olympics did nothing to lower tension in Europe, Hitler's behaviour there increasing animosity. More recently a war was started in Central America by a riot following a football match, and an ice-hockey match between the USSR and Czechoslovakia revived all the tension between these nations after the 1968 invasion and began a riot. We have already noted the Birmingham report[82] (p95), which submitted that violence among football players can spark off violence among the spectators.

The common factor between Waskow's and Flugel's ideas is the notion of a supra-national organisation, and, of course, we have such an organisation in the United Nations. As I write this chapter we are in the aftermath of the Indo-Pakistan war throughout which the Security Council of the United Nations was paralysed by the veto of the Soviet Union. Most of the British newspapers are scoffing at the whole organisation, tending to write it off as a 'dismal failure' or as completely ineffective in its central peacekeeping function. What they tend to forget is that the organisation is only a quarter of a century old and the failure they are pinpointing is in its most difficult task. In view of what we have learned in this book, is it likely that the United Nations or any other machinery could prevent war immediately?

Looked at historically in terms of the lack of international cooperation of the past, the rise of internationalism in this century is as spectacular and breathtaking as some of our recent technological advances. Leaving aside its failures, the United Nations has had some remarkable successes: it stopped the fighting in Cyprus, it has several times reduced the fighting between Israel and Egypt, and the first move towards settling the Berlin blockade came from casual conversations held at the United Nations. Even the much derided League of Nations, which is usually quoted as a failure, may have sown the seeds for the more sophisticated United Nations.

In many ways it is the unpublished and informal activities

of the UN which are the most important. Frank[197] reported the results of a questionnaire that was circulated to seventy-five randomly selected members of national missions by'Best: 86 per cent of those who answered said they had more contact with diplomats from other countries than they would at a post in a national capital, 82 per cent found these contacts to be less formal, two-thirds found it easier to exchange off-the-record information, and 90 per cent said they had more contact with delegates from unfriendly countries. In a brief analysis of the psychological features of the UN Frank[197] suggests it has the following beneficial functions: (1) delegates from all nations can meet on neutral ground, which means that not only can formal negotiations be easily carried out but distortions based on national stereotypes can be corrected and informal proposals can be offered without commitment; (2) by formally appealing to the UN as a forum, nations can place their national prestige 'on deposit' in a crisis, thus gaining time; (3) the fact that delegates must fill multiple roles forces them to be fair in dealing with each other, for one day a member is defending his national interests, and the next he is trying to be an impartial chairman of a committee; and (4) international attitudes weaken nationalistic ones. Frank suggests three ways in which the UN is directly promoting peace: by breaking down national stereotypes, by training politicians for international cooperation, and by creating a world public opinion.

International cooperation, the struggle for objectives other than national interests, perhaps eventually the subjugation of national sovereignty to international law, seem to be the methods by which man is currently stumbling towards peaceful coexistence. The European Common Market seems to be yet another exercise in this same vein. Travel and tourism all contribute to this pattern. Almost every trade and profession has its own international association. Theoretically this would seem to be the only process, however slow it proves to be, which will finally reduce conflict. The aim is to produce a single group—'mankind'—to which all individuals can feel in-group loyalty and which will thereby have the authority to deal with the inevitable sub-group conflicts by arbitration, international law, or police action, if necessary.

If international cooperation and loyalty can even begin, then arms control, which is essential for man to survive, can also begin. Here again progress, however slight, has been made in this century. Furthermore, as cooperation becomes more extensive—perhaps, as I have suggested, in the anti-pollution battle—detailed plans to relieve tension, frustration and hardship in the less fortunate parts of the world can be thrashed out. Finally, an established hierarchy of nations, to which all peoples can subscribe, together with a truly international arbitration forum, plus police service, can be developed. If such a system did develop, it would be tantamount to world government but would not involve the complete loss of sovereignty and ability to participate which that ominous term seems to imply; indeed it could only work if participation and universal need fulfilment were realities.

Reduction of Criminal Violence

The importance of weapons control has already been stressed. Firm social controls and stable hierarchies at all levels are specially important if crime of any kind is to be kept to an acceptable minimum. Sometimes we are apt to forget how recently our relatively sophisticated methods of social control have been developed. It was not until 1748 that the Bow Street Runners were introduced into England. Pitt tried to introduce a Police Bill in 1785, but this attempt failed in the face of strenuous opposition. However, a marine police force was established in 1798 because of the enormous losses of stock by theft from the West India docks in London. The Luddite riots of 1811, the Corn Law riots of 1815, and the Spa Fields riots of 1816, were all dealt with by the military, and the Peterloo massacre of ordinary men, women and children at Manchester in 1819 demonstrated how crude and ineffective such methods were. Peel did not introduce his police bill until 1829.[11]

When we turn to individual acts of violent crime, we have to think of the environment in which an individual is reared and the training he receives, the stresses and strains he is currently suffering, and the external constraints put upon him by the controlling social forces and by public attitudes. The latter social sanctions may be extremely powerful, not only inhibiting action at a moment of tension but also contributing to our social training. Almost every culture feels that wilful murder is morally wrong. Undoubtedly this powerful feeling is a factor in inhibiting us from committing the act when we are angry enough and hate enough. Who has never experienced a murderous thought? In our culture most of us also feel pretty strongly that it is wrong to rob somebody by threatening violence, but we are less certain about the degree of sin involved in reckless driving (which not infrequently has fatal consequences), or breaking the speed limit. It is my belief that, while all these events are criminal and contain some measure of violence, the social controls applied have to be tempered by the prevailing social mores. Murder, robbery, carrying weapons of violence, settling disputes by thuggery, etc, are acceptable to so few people that we can afford to examine the offenders on a fairly individual basis. In other words, we can operate the principle that these offences are unacceptable to the majority and, therefore, we need to discover and deal with the individuals who, for one reason or another, do not conform to the social mores. Having discovered such people, we can then ask ourselves why are they not conforming, whether their nonconformity is dangerous and, if so, in what way is it dangerous and how can we stop it recurring. With violence such as road violence, however, we have a different problem. It is so socially acceptable that a group approach is necessary—in other words, society's first task, if it is going to protect itself, is to make the currently acceptable behaviour unacceptable. Courts, punishments and the like are reflections of public opinion and, therefore, on their own cannot operate against the social mores—hence the current disparity of treatment between the criminal who uses a gun as his weapon and the one who uses a car. Because of this I shall deal with road violence separately and tackle the socially unacceptable crimes of violence first.

Our first thoughts are bound to turn towards the legal sanctions, or sentences, as operated by the courts. These are supposed to fulfil three functions—retribution, deterrence and prevention. How retributive we wish to be depends upon the ethical structure of our society and is in itself a reflection of the violence of the society. In previous centuries, crimes of all sorts were considered to deserve sanctioned violence such as the rack, the thumbscrew, flogging, burning at the stake, hanging and quartering, decapitation and so forth. Deterrence is very difficult to evaluate because, as a large proportion of crime goes undetected, we do not know what fluctuations in the level of actual behaviour (as opposed to that which finds its way into the criminal statistics) we are dealing with. All we can say is that on a psychological level it seems unlikely that the rational businesslike evaluation procedure which deterrence is supposed to involve, the weighing of costs against benefits, plays much part when an angry man strikes out at his wife or two drunks are having a fight, or a sex-crazed man is hunting for a rape victim. If any offenders (let us say in the case of robbery) do make such calculations, most of them will be misinformed because they are unlikely to read official law reports; they must also be aware of court inconsistency and their previous experience may have taught them first-hand that detection is unlikely.

Prevention can either operate by removing a potentially violent person to an institution, by interfering with the environment that produced the violence, or by trying to effect a fundamental change in the individual concerned. To take the last point first, we have already seen how a few people may be violent because of illness, and clearly they require medical treatment, but I have also indicated that some people are violent products of a violent training system, of a violent past. Like the rest of us the latter are not going to change very much by being sent to an institution, or having detailed discussions with doctors, or taking tablets. The stability of society depends to some extent on the stability and predictability of adult human personality. It should not surprise us that once they have attained maturity people retain their individual response set to environmental stimuli, and pressures to conform (or to do anything else) only produce limited change. The judge who says 'Let this be a lesson to you' should remember that, whether it is a lesson or not, the man in the dock shares the same biological limitations as he does himself. Neither is likely to change in a massive way.

This brings us to the removal of the potentially violent man to an institution. In Britain there used to be a sentence of 'preventive detention' to enable courts to give long prison sentences to persistently dangerous people. Recently it has been modified to a less rigorous 'extended sentence', because it had been found that the men receiving the PD sentences were not violent dangerous people at all but inadequate, lonely, petty but persistent thieves; courts were more confident about predicting their repeated offending than with the violent criminal. Walker, Hammond and Steer[198] have argued that a number of violent offences on an offender's record should be considered as a possible reason for a long sentence of imprisonment. In the same pamphlet however Carr-Hill[199] has set out very cogent statistical arguments against this notion, and pointed out that most of the violence-prone people have not yet been convicted of violence. To be certain of preventing most of violent recidivism, one would have to give very long sentences to all violent first offenders, and this would be ethically unjustifiable. Carr-Hill could have added that there can be a world of difference between the persistently violent man (say the drunkard who gets into fights with other drunkards fairly regularly) and the really dangerous man (say a man who, in a fit of rage, will perhaps kill several people), and that, as persistence and dangerousness are not always related, preventive imprisonment based on previous records may well omit many of the really dangerous people.

Perhaps we pay too little attention in our social control system to our third possible method of prevention—interference with the environment. Courts have very limited power to interfere with anything other than the offender, but they can order that he be supervised, for example, by a probation officer. This, of course, can add a new dimension to an offender's world—a father figure to the developing and immature, a counsellor and leaning post to those under severe strain, a friend to the lonely, perhaps drunken and desperate, individual. We are still a long way from the time when, after the examination of a case in some detail, a court can order a special grant or pension to be given to a particular family, or a local authority can be given the responsibility of finding accommodation for someone.

The best immediate environmental device we could establish for the prevention of violence or further violence is a special centre within each densely populated urban area which would provide a consultation and referral service for anybody who requested it and where professionals of all kinds could meet.[167] At present people in difficulties find themselves on a never-ending treadmill of visits to this hospital, that clinic, the other office, and each time they may be dealt with as a newcomer. A basic centre, visited by professionals, with direct links to hostels, sheltered workshops, rehabilitation units, prisons, hospitals and the like would help to coordinate existing facilities, produce a crop of familiar faces and help prevent the type of disaster that overtook the two patients described earlier (p158).

These ideas are generated from British experience but they are not very different from the neighbourhood schemes, with their action task forces and centres, recommended to assist with the prevention of racial violence in the USA by the

President's National Advisory Commission on Civil Disorders.[122]

Control of Riots and Public Violence

With international television available it is interesting to see how different national police forces cope with riots and the like. Forces specifically trained to deal with these problems and trained to contain and cool rather than fight it out are better than the untrained. This point was made quite forcibly by the National Advisory Committee on Civil Disorders: 'Despite the obvious importance of well-trained police in controlling disorder, the Commission survey of the capabilities of selected police departments disclosed serious deficiencies... The control of civil disturbances... requires large numbers of disciplined personnel... organised and trained to work as a team under a highly unified command and control system.'

There are two points that are not always publicly made, although they may be well understood privately. Firstly, the nature of the weapons used should depend upon the objectives aimed at. If the rioters are ordinary citizens and are not attacking in any military sense, then containment and control is all that is needed and weapons should be matched not bettered. Secondly, the nature of the violence should be understood in a sociological sense by any police or military commanders before really appropriate and, therefore, effective action can be taken. For example, in Northern Ireland there was a long period during which it was genuinely believed that IRA violence was the product of a few 'criminals'—it was unsanctioned criminal violence in the usual sense. So it was to the Protestant majority, but to the Catholic minority it was sanctioned. If that had been fully appreciated, internment would never have been introduced; it would have been realised that it was no use treating the IRA as eccentric individuals and gaoling them, since virtually the whole community was angry and prepared to fight, and internment would exacerbate its anger.

Control of the Assaultative Individual

In an American study, Toch[104] arranged a research programme in which thirty-two policemen who had suffered assaults, nineteen men who had assaulted policemen, forty-four prisoners, and thirty-three parolees with violent records were interviewed by a team of people who themselves could have qualified as subjects in that they, too, were policemen, offenders, parolees etc—exact peers of the actual subjects. The programme arrived at a number of interesting conclusions, such as the ineffectiveness of deterrence against violent men, but here we should particularly note its findings that violence-prone people invite violence-prone interactions with others, and that violence-prone games tend to be played by men who feel unsure of their status or identity. These considerations applied to both offenders and victims; particular policemen, for instance, were much more likely to provoke a violent incident than some of their colleagues. They suggest that any violence-prone person (professional or offender) should be given insight into his conduct and if possible should be retrained. For the police they suggest a detailed course of instruction with the objective of making non-violence the only really acceptable policeman-like conduct.

It has also been my experience in counselling work that some professionals are more likely to provoke violence than others. One psychiatrist I know working in a busy emergency department has been assaulted two or three times and had his office smashed up twice. None of his colleagues have suffered these misfortunes even when seeing exactly the same patients.

For the purposes of discussion, there are a number of fairly didactic guidelines which I have found useful. When a disturbed person is being interviewed, he should not feel trapped or in any way be humiliated or made to feel inferior. Violence, it should be remembered, is partly a means of climbing a hierarchy, so if the social distance is reduced by informality, helpfulness, a cosy office, there is less need for violence. Violence is also a means of communication, and if the interviewer is oblique or obstructive, the angry man may communicate his feelings more directly. A simple and clear indication that the message has been received and understood can reduce tension; it may even be necessary to say: 'I can see you are going to hit me; you don't have to do that, I will do what I can'. At no point should threats or counter-threats be made, for these will certainly lead to violence; and remarks such as 'You wouldn't dare hit me' are tantamount to calling the client 'chicken' and stirring all his inferiority feelings—so that his only honourable way out is to prove you wrong. After the first few difficult encounters with a new client the best way of preventing violence is an understanding working relationship in which mutual trust and respect have been established.

It is also worth remembering that drunken men cannot be argued with and should be allowed to sleep, sit quietly, or given tea, with the reassurance that discussion will follow later; and that when in a violent mood psychotic or mad individuals can be much more dangerous than the hysterical, the drunken, or the psychopathic because they may have delusional ideas which are not open to discussion. If violence-prone clients are expected, there should be more than one professional in the vicinity. If things get out of hand, no one should be ashamed or too guilt-ridden to draw others (preferably other skilled professionals) into the situation. To do this is not an admission of defeat but the next skilful move, and it should be remembered that the police are professionals who are used to handling violence. If nobody can be found, then drawing the conflict into the open or a public place is the next best thing, always remembering that property is less valuable than flesh and blood.

In an institutional setting tensions, and violent feelings, can be greater, partly because they are exacerbated and communicated by the group mechanisms mentioned in Chapter 6 and partly because the frustrations of institutional life can be higher. Every prison governor knows that the fruits of mismanagement can be hideous riots. A remarkable experiment in prison management has been conducted in England at Grendon prison. Although a maximum security prison, escapes are unknown and it is remarkably relaxed and tension-free. The majority of inmates are, like the rest of the British prison population, persistent recidivists with large numbers of personal and social problems. No unwilling prisoner is forced to go to Grendon but the prison does take its fair share of violent 'unmanageable' men. It is significant that, even so, violence between prisoners and against uniformed staff is at a very low level. For example, sex offenders, who have to be secluded for their own protection in every other prison, mix freely and are unmolested at Grendon. Tensions, of course, occur within the prison but they are dealt with by group discussion, even as an emergency procedure if necessary. In the discussions verbal hostility is allowed and communications are privileged in that they cannot be followed by staff retribution and punishment. The attention-seeking aspects of violent behaviour are played down as far as possible, and if a man has a tantrum, or if a fight does occur, these occurrences will result in discussion but not in punishment or solitary confinement. At Grendon violence or the threat of violence is no escape route, and the same ends can always be achieved by verbal means.

Reduction of Road Violence

As already stressed, this problem is of a different nature from the control of other types of criminal violence, partly because, although technically criminal, it is semi-sanctioned and partly because we are dealing with a mixture of problems, some related to the aggressive urges we have discussed in this book, and some related to the limitations of human ability and engineering. Frequently observers comment that there will be no reduction in violence on the road until psychologists find a way of changing man's nature. I wish to disagree with this view because (a) road death-rates have steadily de-

clined since the 1930s (absolute figures are up because there
have been population increases and an increase in road transport) and (b) we cannot wait that long.

The first essential, which is slightly out of context in this
book, is the engineering problem. We must study and understand ordinary driving behaviour and modify our roads and
cars accordingly. Of course, this is exactly what is happening
—motorways, proper lighting, seat belts, better braking systems and so on are all attempts to solve this problem, and
they have brought results. Road fatalities per registered motor
vehicle decrease as the number of motor vehicles per person
increases. Road fatalities in a given country can, to a large
extent, be predicted from a knowledge of the population size
and the number of motor vehicles.[200]

There are two psychological problems—how to improve
skill and how to change attitudes. We have talked of training
in other situations but here it is vital; if a driver is trained
firstly to drive skilfully and secondly to drive non-aggressively,
no fundamental changes in his nature will have occurred but
he will be less likely to cause an accident. Pretty obvious
really but some countries (eg, Belgium) still have no driving
test and in Britain we spend very little on driver training,
in spite of the evidence of the value of training. In 1935
the Metropolitan Police Driving School was opened, at which
time the accident rate in the force was 1 per 9,000 miles; by
1939 it had fallen to 1 per 25,000 miles, and in 1954 it was
1 per 72,587 miles.[201]

Road safety campaigns are regularly held in Britain, but
there is no indication that they are beginning to change public attitudes from sanctioning to non-sanctioning aggressive
driving. They are rather of the 'go carefully', 'be a good boy'
type of approach, and are rarely supported by effective polic-
ing. Perhaps the single most effective element in preventing
aggressive and illegal driving is the visible policeman. An
experiment was conducted in Lancashire, England, before
World War II which illustrates this point and indicates what

can be done and how to do it. Between 1931 and 1935 a campaign of inconspicuous patrols and heavy penalties had been introduced; public hostility went up, accidents went up. As an alternative in 1938 concentrated forces of police patrolled the roads where accidents most frequently occurred. Motorists were advised of their faults rather than prosecuted and sometimes they were singled out in traffic jams for criticism by loud-hailer. Parking offenders were sent warning letters pointing out the dangers of bad parking, and a map showing proper parking places. Similar letters were sent to other minor offenders. A collateral press and poster campaign was run in conjunction with the exercise, which became known as the 'Courtesy Cop Scheme' and achieved a 44 per cent reduction in casualties.[201] An official report commented:

> The result so far has certainly been to create a spirit of co-operation between the motorist and the Police, to an extent which has made the average driver tend to regard a fellow motorist who has been prosecuted as the recipient of a well-deserved public rebuke, rather than viewing him sympathetically as a victim of Police 'persecution'. In other words, a motoring offence is ceasing to be considered something to boast about but is being regarded, far more properly, as a breach of good manners.[201]

The war put a stop to the scheme and as far as I know it has not been tried again, though it is difficult to fathom why not. A recent smaller experiment has been tried in the North of England, in the same spirit, in order to combat the hazards of fog on fast motorways, where, for some reason, drivers will not sufficiently reduce their speed. This scheme has involved flooding the fogbound motorway with police patrols, which then pilot the traffic at the correct and safe speed.

The Courtesy Cop Scheme illustrates a point about punishment that we are beginning to understand more clearly from psychological experiments. Because we all work within a punishment/reward framework in life, we sometimes tend to think of punishment as simply unwanted unpleasantness. If it is to produce change, punishment has to be specially tailored to a particular situation. Very often it is essential for the punishment to follow the undesired behaviour *immediately*, not hours or days afterwards. Furthermore, an appropriate punishment such as imprisonment for a minor offence may be ineffective, even negative, because of resentment and self-justification. It is interesting that the police found the loud-hailer to be effective—punishment sure enough, but very cheap, acceptable, and sensible. Even the Courtesy Cop Scheme did not emphasise the reward side of the punishment/reward equation. Why can't we think of carrots as well as sticks? What would be wrong with introducing a graded licence system, the bottom grade only entitling the owner to a small car and slow speeds; greater flexibility and privilege would be earned by good conduct, eg, points awarded for accident-free periods, courtesy endorsements by police patrols, good marks in voluntary driving tests?

As far as alcohol goes we are beginning to learn the lessons and many countries are now introducing stricter, objective, drinking and driving rules; but we still have to get round the attitudinal problem. Drunken driving is grossly dangerous, turning John Citizen into a potentially violent maniac, and yet people who indulge themselves in this way are still not condemned by public opinion.

References to this chapter appear on pp190-91

10 *Conclusions*

Violence, then, is an almost universal mammalian phenomenon: it does not occur randomly, chaotically, but is related to masculinity, to the anatomical apparatus and weaponry available, to the degree of frustration and stress inherent in a particular situation, to the type of previous experience and training received, to health, to attitudes both personal and public, to love, to hate. It is not a homogeneous phenomenon, for there are many different types of violence—pathological, sanctioned, unsanctioned, domestic, criminal, road, group, war. Each is best considered on its own terms.

This book has made the tacit assumption that for every act of violence there is a reason, a predisposing factor. The avenues we have explored have indicated only too clearly how little we know about those reasons, but we are perhaps able to sketch a hazy outline of the background cause for any particular violent event if we study it in enough detail. Why should we be interested in such causes? Probably for two basic reasons—curiosity and the danger to ourselves. It is my hope that this book will whet your curiosity further; but no book is likely significantly to alter the level of danger unless we as a community come to understand that violence does have complex causes and then try to analyse what those causes might be. Then we may be able to effect some measure of control and so reduce the danger.

Sometimes our first realisation that aggression is inherent in the nature of man and in his success as a creature leads to the argument that nothing short of a complete change of his whole psychological and social make-up will lead to the elimination of violence. No creature can suddenly, within one generation, say, change into a new kind of creature (that is the extent of the change desired by some) simply because evolution is long-winded by our ordinary time-scales. Those who argue that the nature of man must be changed overnight do not tell us how to do it—presumably it is supposed to happen by thinking about it. Panaceas of all sorts are unlikely to work because as we have seen violence is never unidimensional, and the attitudinal dimension is almost never tackled by the quick easy solution.

Attitudes are indeed a key factor, and whenever we consider the problem of violence control we should urgently ask ourselves whether we are serious or not. We may not be. Some of the simplistic remedies just mentioned are so self-defeating that one suspects they may be rationalisations that allow us to pay lip service to the notion of violence control while avoiding a change in the status quo; indeed they may actually allow us to increase our own levels of vicarious violence. Are we really being serious when we suggest that the solution to criminal violence is to have more sanctioned state violence such as hanging, flogging and the like? Are we really being serious when detailed report after detailed report outlining solutions to race riots are consistently ignored (see the conclusion to the President's National Advisory Commission on Civil Disorders)?[122] Are we really being serious when we buy and sell arms for financial, purely national, or purely personal reasons without evaluating the social cost? We do not even know if man is capable, at this stage in his history, of being serious in his attempts to control violence. Even if we want to, will we be able to make any progress towards reducing the violence in the world? Will we only vote for politicians who put international collaboration at the top of their list of priorities; will we ignore all the deep-rooted feelings we have about our group, our nation, and try to accommodate other people's requirements to the detriment of our own; will we press for penal reform so that more rational treatment can be offered to criminals; will we support measures that will cut down violence by automobiles, such as stricter road rules, larger police forces, elaborate driving instruction, expensive standards of car safety; will we support a wide-scale ban on firearms? You and I probably won't support many of these actions and yet we still say we are concerned about violence. We are probably not yet serious enough, although our concern is a step in the right direction.

Once again then, 'How do we change attitudes?' Certainly not quickly, though here I cannot resist the temptation to add four of my own panaceas to the already long list. We need to foster international collaboration and communication at all levels—diplomatic, scientific, social, sporting—and the institutions we have already developed, including the United Nations and its subsidiaries, may be the best way of doing this. We need to take active political steps to eliminate social grievances, which include genuine listening to protests, the establishment of machinery for protest and grievance to filter up from the bottom to the top of a society, and a reduction of the gaps between one section of a community and another, between one nation and another. We need positively to introduce a programme of non-violence into our educational systems; even though we should be hard pressed this minute to spell out the details of such a programme, we should begin thinking and experimenting about it. We need to establish effective social services for people in distress, agencies to which the inadequate or the psychopathic can turn with a guarantee of assistance, and caring systems which will reduce the damage sustained by children in unsatisfactory homes. None of these suggestions is original, none unorthodox, but all require money, lots of money. Once again then are we serious?

Certainly in part the solution to the violence problem is a reallocation of international resources. If we are really serious then that reallocation will come because we will put violence control at the top of our list of priorities. Equally if we are not serious it won't.

Are we then caught in some kind of nightmarish vicious circle? No, there are grounds for optimism. The very concern that manifests itself in a search for answers to the problem is already a glimmer of hope, but much more substantial than that, most of the methods of violence control that have been suggested have already begun. Often we are told that violence is on the increase, but this is at least debatable, and there seems to be a genuine view of war as a problem: very few modern communities regard war as desirable even when they indulge in it. The gloomiest of the pessimists regard violence as necessary for human existence, but this is not supported by the facts; violence is an exceptional blot on a peaceable existence for most of the world's population. Aggression does seem to be an integral part of mammalian life, but even in man violence is very much a last resort.

It seems to me that the abolition of aggression is both unlikely and undesirable. What we need to achieve is the reduction of violence to a barely perceptible minimum. We need to create a new and powerful set of taboos. Many other creatures, including other primates, have stronger antiviolence taboos than we have. Until the technological breakthrough of sophisticated toolmaking some 40,000 years ago it was unimportant to have this particular taboo, but now it is required increasingly urgently and we may yet achieve it in time.

A final speculative point worth raising for discussion because it has been implicit in much of this book is that human society is largely regulated by two separate, sometimes opposing, sometimes complementary, forces—aggression and altruism. Aggression is the basis of the competitive need for personal victory; and altruism, concerned with the group, with the species as a whole, subjugates individual desires to group needs. At the simplest level 'I want' has to be modified by the needs of others unless we are to run into headlong collision with them. Altruism enables us to accommodate the other man's needs, perhaps because eventually the species and hence the individual (though a different one) is best served this way. Patriotism is in part an aggressive force, because 'my country' really means 'me and my group' against 'them', but it is also altruistic in that a really patriotic individual will often sacrifice all his personal needs, even his life quite willingly, for his country. In doing this he has modified his personal needs for the benefit of the group, because in survival terms the group he belongs to has to survive before any one individual can survive. All altruistic acts can be seen as means of promoting group survival. The more altruistic (and, therefore, the less self-interested) a particular act appears, the broader the group to which it is related. Perhaps we are in a phase of becoming more altruistic by broadening our horizons beyond the family, the tribe, the nation, to the species as a whole. As we have seen, unless we do this the species is in mortal danger; but if we do it, then group survival is highly likely.

References

1 *INTRODUCTION* (pp13-19)

1 Storr, A. *Human Aggression* (Harmondsworth, 1968)
2 Tiger, L. *Men in Groups* (1969)
3 Daniels, D. N. & Gilula, M. F. 'Violence and the Struggle for Existence', *Violence and the Struggle for Existence*, ed by D. N. Daniels, M. F. Gilula, & F. M. Ochberg (Boston, 1970)
4 Darwin, C. *The Descent of Man*, revised ed (1883)
5 Lorenz, K. *On Aggression*, trans by M. Latzke (1966)
6 Scott, J. P. *Aggression* (Chicago, 1958)
7 Hinde, R. A. 'Aggression Again', *New Society* (Feb 1969), 291-2
8 Bray, W. *The Everyday Life of the Aztecs* (1968)
9 Taft, P. & Ross, P. 'American Labor Violence: Its Causes, Character & Outcome', *The History of Violence in America*, ed by H. D. Graham & T. R. Gurr (New York, 1969)
10 Roberts, B. C. 'On the Origins and Resolution of English Working-Class Protest', *The History of Violence in America*, ed by H. D. Graham & T. R. Gurr (New York, 1969)
11 Hibbert, C. *The Roots of Evil* (Boston, 1963)

2 *VIOLENCE IN ANIMALS* (pp20-36)

12 Washburn, S. L. & Hamburg, D. A. 'The Study of Primate Behavior', *Primate Behavior*, ed by I. DeVore (New York, 1965)
13 Read, C. 'On the Differentiation of the Human from the Anthropoid Mind', *British Journal of Psychology*, 8 (1917), 395-422
14 DeVore, I. & Hall, K. R. L. 'Baboon Ecology', *Primate Behavior* ed by I. DeVore (New York, 1965)

15 Tinbergen, N. 'On War and Peace in Animals and Man', *Science*, 160 (1968), 1411-18

16 Tinbergen, N. *Social Behaviour in Animals*, second ed (1964)

17 Carpenter, C. R. 'A Field Study in Siam of the Behaviour and Social Relations of the Gibbon', *Comparative Psychological Monographs*, 16 no 5 (1940), 1-212

18 Carpenter, C. R. 'The Howlers of Barro Colorado Island', *Primate Behavior*, ed by I. DeVore (New York, 1965)

19 Southwick, C. H., Beg, M. A. & Siddiqi, M. R. 'Rhesus Monkeys in North India', *Primate Behavior*, ed by I. DeVore (New York, 1965)

20 Van-Lawick Goodall, J. M. 'The Behaviour of Free-Living Chimpanzees in the Gombe Stream Reserve', *Animal Behaviour Monographs*, Vol I, Part 3 (1968)

21 Southwick, C. H. 'Aggressive Behaviour of Rhesus Monkeys in Natural and Captive Groups', *Aggressive Behaviour*, ed by S. Garattini & E. B. Sigg (Amsterdam, 1969)

22 Zuckerman, S. G. *The Social Life of Monkey and Apes* (1932)

23 Hall, K. R. L. & DeVore, I. 'Baboon Social Behavior', *Primate Behavior*, ed by I. DeVore (New York, 1965)

24 Hall, K. R. L. 'Aggression in Monkey & Ape Societies', *The Natural History of Aggression*, ed by J. D. Carthy & F. J. Ebling (1964)

25 Russell, C. & Russell, W. M. S. *Violence, Monkeys and Man*, (1968)

26 Southwick, C. H. 'An Experimental Study of Intragroup Agonistic Behaviour in Rhesus Monkeys', *Behaviour* 28 (1967), 182-209

27 Leyhausen, P. 'The Sane Community—A Density Problem?', *Discovery* (26 Sept 1965), 27-33

28 Calhoun, J. B. 'The Social Use of Space', *Physiological Mammology*, Vol I, ed by W. V. Meyer & R. G. Van Gelder (New York, 1963)

29 Barnett, S. A. *A Study in Behaviour* (1963)

30 Rothballer, A. B. 'Aggression, Defence and Neurohumors', *Aggression and Defence*, ed by C. D. Clemente & D. B. Lindsley (Los Angeles, 1967)

31 Beeman, E. A. 'The Effect of Male Hormone on Aggressive Behaviour in Mice', *Physiological Zoology*, 20 (1947), 373-405

32 Lagerspetz, K. M. J. 'Aggression and Aggressiveness in Laboratory Mice', *Aggressive Behaviour*, ed by S. Garattini & E. B. Sigg (Amsterdam, 1969)

33 Harlow, H. F. & Harlow, M. K. 'Social Deprivation in Monkeys', *Scientific American*, 207 (1962), 137-46

34 Harlow, H. F. & Griffin, G. A. 'Induced Mental and Social Deficits in Rhesus Monkeys', *The Biological Basis of Mental Retardation*, ed by S. F. Osler & R. E. Cooke (Baltimore, 1965)

35 Boelkins, R. C. & Heiser, J. F. 'Biological Bases of Aggression', in *Violence & the Struggle for Existence*, ed by D. N. Daniels, M. F. Gilula & F. M. Ochberg (Boston, 1970)

36 Kahn, M. W. 'Infantile Experiences and Mature Aggressive Behaviour of Mice: Some Maternal Influences', *Journal of Genetic Psychology*, 84 (1954), 65-72

37 Eibl-Eibesfeldt, I. 'Aggressive Behavior and Ritualized Fighting in Animals', *Violence and War*, ed by J. H. Masserman (New York, 1963)

38 Scott, J. P. 'Hostility and Aggression in Animals', *Roots of Behavior*, ed by E. L. Bliss (New York, 1962)

39 Ulrich, R. & Symannek, B. 'Pain as a Stimulus for Aggression', *Aggressive Behaviour*, ed by S. Garattini & E. B. Sigg (Amsterdam, 1969)

40 O'Kelly, L. W. & Steckle, L. C. 'A Note on Long-Enduring Emotional Responses in the Rat', *Journal of Psychology*, 8 (1939), 125

41 Azrin, N. H., Hutchinson, R. R. & McLaughlin, R. 'The Opportunity for Aggression as an Operant Reinforcer during Aversive Stimulation', *Journal of the Experimental Analysis of Behaviour*, 8 (1965), 171

42 Pavlov, I. *Conditioned Reflexes*, trans by G. V. Aurep (1927)

43 Van-Lawick Goodall, J. M. 'Chimpanzees of the Gombe Stream Reserve', in *Primate Behavior*, ed by I. DeVore (New York, 1965)

44 Hinde, R. A. 'The Bases of Aggression in Animals', *Journal of Psychosomatic Research*, 13 (1969), 213-19

45 Seward, J. P. 'Aggressive Behavior in the Rat. I. General Characteristics: Age and Sex Differences', *Journal of Comparative Psychology*, 38 (1945), 175-97

46 Keys, A., Brozek, J., Henscel, A., Michelson, O. & Taylor, H. L. *The Biology of Human Starvation*, Vol II (Minneapolis, 1950)

47 Washburn, S. L. & Hamburg, D. A. 'The Implications of Primate Research', *Primate Behavior*, ed by I. DeVore (New York, 1965)

3 VIOLENT MECHANISMS (pp37-53)

48 Leakey, L. S. B. 'Development of Aggression in Early Human and Pre-Human Evolution', *Aggression and Defense*, ed by C. D. Clemente & D. B. Lindsley (Berkeley, 1967)

49 Bigelow, R. *The Dawn Warriors* (Boston, 1969)

50 Washburn, S. L. 'Role of Conflict in Human Evolution', *Conflict in Society*, ed by A. de Renck & J. Knight (1966)

51 Haskins, C. P. *Of Societies and Men* (1952)

52 Van-Lawick Goodall, J. M. 'Chimpanzees of the Gombe Stream Reserve', *Primate Behavior*, ed by I. DeVore (New York, 1965)

53 Matthews, L. H. 'Overt Fighting in Mammals', *The Natural History of Aggression*, ed by J. D. Carthy & F. J. Ebling (1964)

54 Eibl-Eibesfeldt, I. Ontogenetic and Maturational Studies of Aggressive Behavior', *Aggression and Defense*, ed by C. D. Clemente & D. B. Lindsley (Berkeley, 1967)

55 Kaada, B. 'Brain Mechanisms Related to Aggressive Behavior', *Aggression and Defense*, ed by C. D. Clemente & D. B. Lindsley (Berkeley, 1967)

56 Masserman, J. H. 'Is the Hypothalamus a Center of Emotion?', *Psychosomatic Medicine*, 3 (1941), 3-25

57 Kluver, H. & Bucy, P. C. 'Preliminary Analysis of Functions of the Temporal Lobes in Monkeys', *Archives of Neurology and Psychiatry*, 42 (1939), 979-1,000

58 Brown, J. L. & Hunsperger, R. W. 'Neuroethology and the Motivation of Agonistic Behaviour', *Animal Behaviour*, 11 (1963), 439-48

59 Rosvold, H. E., Mirsky, A. F. & Pribram, K. M. 'Influence of Amygdalectomy on Social Behaviour in Monkeys', *Journal of Comparative and Physiological Psychology*, 47 (1954), 173-8

60 Delgado, J. M. R. 'Offensive-Defensive Behaviour in Free Monkeys and Chimpanzees Induced by Radio Stimulation of the Brain', *Aggressive Behaviour*, ed by S. Garattini & E. B. Sigg (Amsterdam, 1969)

61 Delgado, J. M. R. 'Aggression and Defense under Cerebral Radio Control', *Aggression and Defense*, ed by C. D. Clemente & D. B. Lindsley (Berkeley, 1967)

62 Hare, R. D. 'Psychopathy, Autonomic Functioning and the Orienting Response', *Journal of Abnormal Psychology*, monograph supplement no 73 (1968)

4 *PSYCHOLOGY OF VIOLENCE* (pp54-72)

63 Montagu, M. F. A. *Man and Aggression* (1968)

64 Dollard, J., Miller, N. E., Doob, L. W., Mowrer, O. H. & Sears, R. R. *Frustration and Aggression* (1944).

65 Sears, R. R., Hovland, C. I. & Miller, N. E. 'Minor Studies of Aggression. I. Measurement of Aggressive Behaviour', *Journal of Psychology*, 9 (1940), 275-95

66 Rycroft, C. *A Critical Dictionary of Psychoanalysis* (1968)

67 Fromm, E. *Man for Himself* (New York, 1947)

68 Freud, A. *The Ego and the Mechanisms of Defence* (1937)

69 Freud, S. 'Formulations on the Two Principles of Mental Functioning', *Standard Edition of Complete Psychological Works of Sigmund Freud*, trans by J. Strachey (1964)

70 Freud, S. *Three Essays on the Theory of Sexuality*, fourth edition, trans by J. Strachey (1949)

71 Klein, M. *Envy and Gratitude* (1957)

72 Hovland, C. I. & Sears, R. R. 'Minor Studies of Aggression: VI Correlations of Lynchings with Economic Indices', *Journal of Psychology*, 9 (1940), 301-10

73 Allport, G. W. *The Nature of Prejudice* (Cambridge, Mass, 1954)

74 Adorno, T. W., Frenkel-Brunswik, E., Levinson, D. J. & Sanford, R. N. *The Authoritarian Personality* (New York, 1952)

75 Douglas, J. W. B., Ross, J. M. & Simpson, H. R. *All Our Future* (1968)

76 Nye, F. I. 'Child Adjustment in Broken and Unhappy Unbroken Homes', *Marriage and Family Living*, 19 (1957), 356-61

77 Lewis, H. *Deprived Children* (1954)

78 Wardle, C. J. 'Two Generations of Broken Homes in the Genesis of Conduct and Behaviour Disorders in Childhood', *British Medical Journal*, ii (1961), 349-54

79 Sears, R. R., Maccoby, E. E. & Levin, H. *Patterns of Child Rearing* (New York, 1957)

80 Bandura, A. & Walters, R. H. *Social Learning and Personality Development* (New York, 1963)

81 Duncan, G. M., Frazier, S. H., Litin, E. M., Johnson, A. M. & Barron, A. J. 'Etiological Factors in First-Degree Murder', *Journal of American Medical Association*, 168 (1958), 1755 8

82 Birmingham Research Group. *Soccer Hooliganism* (Bristol, 1968)

83 Bandura, A., Ross, D. & Ross, S. A. 'Vicarious Reinforcement and Imitative Learning', *Journal of Abnormal and Social Psychology*, 67 (1963), 601-7

84 Albert, R. S. 'The Role of Mass Media and the Effect of Aggressive Film Content upon Children's Aggressive Responses and Identification Choices', *Genetic Psychological Monographs*, 55 (1957), 221-85

85 Himmelweit, H. T., Oppenheim, A. M. & Vince, P. *Television and the Child* (1958)

86 Schramm, W., Lyle, J. & Parker, E. B. *Television in the Lives of Our Children* (Stanford, Calif, 1961)

87 Hartley, R. E. 'The Impact of Viewing "Aggression" ': 'Studies and Problems of Extrapolation', by J. T. Klapper, *Violence and the Mass Media*, ed by O. N. Larsen (New York, 1968)

88 Milgram, S. 'Behavioural Study of Obedience', *Journal of Abnormal and Social Psychology*, 67 (1963), 371-8

89 Milgram, S. 'Conditioning of Obedience and Disobedience to Authority', *International Journal of Psychiatry*, 6 (1968), 259

5 *SOCIAL FACTORS AND INDIVIDUAL VIOLENCE* (pp73-84)

90 Morris, D. *The Human Zoo* (1969)

91 Carstairs, G. M. 'Overcrowding and Human Aggression', *The History of Violence in America*, ed by H. D. Graham & T. R. Gurr (New York, 1969)

92 Richardson, L. F. *Statistics of Deadly Quarrels* (Pittsburgh, 1960)

93 Cipolla, C. *The Economic History of World Population* (Harmondsworth, 1962)

94 Thomas, D. S. *Social Aspects of the Business Cycle* (1925)

95 Henry, A. F. & Short, J. F. *Suicide and Homicide* (Glencoe, Ill, 1954)

96 Merton, R. K. 'Social Structure and Anomie', *The Sociology of Crime and Delinquency*, ed by M. E. Wolfgang, L. Savitz & N. Johnston (New York, 1962)

97 Durkheim, E. *Suicide*, trans by J. A. Spaulding & G. Simpson (Glencoe, Ill, 1951)

98 Durkheim, E. 'The Normal and the Pathological', *The Sociology of Crime and Delinquency*, ed by M. E. Wolfgang, L. Savitz & N. Johnston (New York, 1962)

99 Glueck, S. 'Theory and Fact in Criminology', *British Journal of Delinquency*, 7 (1956), 92-109

100 Shaw, C. R. & McKay, H. D. 'An Ecological Analysis of Chicago', *The Sociology of Crime and Delinquency*, ed by M. E. Wolfgang, L. Savitz & N. Johnston (New York, 1962)

101 Morris, T. *The Criminal Area* (1957)

102 Wolfgang, M. E. & Ferracuti, F. *The Subculture of Violence* (1967)

103 Fannin, L. F. & Clinard, M. B. 'Differences in the Conception of Self as a Male among Lower & Middle Class Delinquents', *Social Problems*, 13 (1965), 205-14

104 Toch, H. *Violent Men* (Chicago, 1969)

105 Brown, R. M. 'Historical Patterns of Violence in America', *The History of Violence in America*, ed by H. D. Graham & T. R. Gurr (New York, 1969)

106 Daniels, D. N., Trickett, E. J., Shapiro, M. M., Tinklenberg, J. R. & Jackman, J. M. 'The Gun Law Controversy', *Violence and the Struggle for Existence*, ed by D. N. Daniels, M. F. Gilula & F. M. Ochberg (Boston, 1970)

107 Gillin, J. C. & Ochberg, F. M. 'Firearms Control and Violence', *Violence and the Struggle for Existence*, ed by D. N. Daniels, M. F. Gilula & F. M. Ochberg (Boston, 1970)

6 *GROUP VIOLENCE* (pp85-106)

108 Sumner, W. G. 'Folkways', *Sociological Theory*, third edition, ed by L. A. Coser & B. Rosenberg (Toronto, 1969)

109 Blake, R. R. & Mouton, J. S. 'Loyalty of Representatives to In-Group Positions during Intergroup Competition', *Sociometry*, 24 (1961), 177-83

110 Sprott, W. J. H. *Human Groups* (Harmondsworth, 1958)
111 Thrasher, F. M. *The Gang* (Chicago, 1926)
112 Yablonsky, L. *The Violent Gang* (New York, 1962)
113 Cohen, A. *Delinquent Boys—The Culture of the Gang* (Glencoe, Ill, 1955)
114 Cloward, R. A. & Ohlin, L. E. *Delinquency and Opportunity* (Glencoe, Ill, 1961)
115 Mays, J. B. *Growing up in the City* (Liverpool, 1954)
116 Mays, J. B. *Crime and its Treatment* (1970)
117 Scott, P. D. 'Gangs and Delinquent Groups in London', *British Journal of Delinquency*, 7 (1950), 8-21
118 Gibbens, T. C. N. 'Hooliganism and Vandalism', *Medico-Legal Journal*, 38 (1970), 122-34
119 Cohen, S. 'The Politics of Vandalism', *New Society* (12 Dec 1968), 872-4
120 Tilly, C. 'Collective Violence in European Perspective', *The History of Violence in America*, ed by H. D. Graham & T. R. Gurr (New York, 1969)
121 Gurr, T. R. 'A Comparative Study of Civil Strife', *The History of Violence in America*, ed by H. D. Graham & T. R. Gurr (New York, 1969)
122 National Advisory Commission on Civil Disorders. *Report* (US Govt Printing Office, 1968)
123 Caplan, N. S. & Paige, J. M. 'A Study of Ghetto Rioters', *Scientific American*, 219:2 (1968), 15-21
124 Wright, Q. *A Study of War* (Chicago, 1942)
125 Vayda, A. P. 'Hypotheses about the Functions of War', *War—The Anthropology of Armed Conflict & Aggression*, ed by M. Fried, M. Harris & R. Murphy (New York, 1967)
126 Leeds, A. 'The Functions of War', *Violence and War*, ed by J. H. Masserman (New York, 1963)
127 Holsti, O. R. 'The 1914 Case', *American Political Science Review*, 59 (1965), 365-78
128 Rogow, A. A. 'Disability in High Office', *Medical Opinion and Review* (April, 1966), 16-19

7 *VIOLENCE IN DISEASE* (pp107-24)

129 Hill, J. D. 'Aggression and Mental Illness', *The Natural History of Aggression*, ed by J. D. Carthy & F. J. Ebling (New York, 1964)
130 Hill, J. D. & Pond, D. A. 'Reflections on One Hundred Capital Cases Submitted to Electroencephalography', *Journal of Mental Science*, 98 (1952), 23-43
131 Mark, V. H. & Ervin, F. R. *Violence and the Brain* (NY, 1970)
132 Narabayashi, H. & Uns, M. 'Long Range Results in Stereotaxic Amygdalotomy for Behaviour Disorders', *Confina Neurologica*, 27 (1966), 168-71

133 Gunn, J. C. & Fenton, G. 'Epilepsy in Prisons: A Diagnostic Survey', *British Medical Journal*, iv (1969), 326-9

134 Gunn, J. C. & Fenton, G. 'Epilepsy, Automatism & Crime', *Lancet*, i (1971), 1,173-6

135 West, D. J. *Murder Followed by Suicide* (1965)

136 Wolfgang, M. E. 'An Analysis of Homicide - Suicide', *Journal of Clinical and Experimental Psychopathology*, XIX (1958), 208-18

137 Gibson, E. & Klein, S. *Murder 1957-68*, Home Office Research Studies No 3 (1969)

138 Kendell, R. E. 'Relationship Between Aggression and Depression', *Archives of General Psychiatry*, 22 (1970), 308-18

139 Walker, N. *Crime and Insanity in England* (Edinburgh, 1968)

140 Rothstein, D. A. 'Presidential Assassination Syndrome', *Archives of General Psychiatry*, 11 (1964) 245-54

141 Brennan, J. J. 'Mentally Ill Aggressiveness, Popular Delusion or Reality', *American Journal of Psychiatry*, 120 (1964), 1,181-4

142 Shepherd, M. 'Morbid Jealousy: Some Clinical and Social Aspects of a Psychiatric Symptom', *Journal of Mental Science*, 107 (1961), 687-704

143 Henderson, D. K. *Psychopathic States* (New York, 1939)

144 Robins, L. N. *Deviant Children Grown Up* (Baltimore, 1968)

145 Lloyd, R. & Williamson, S. *Born to Trouble* (1968)

146 Guze, S., Goodwin, D. W. & Crane, J. B. 'Criminality and Psychiatric Disorders', *Archives of General Psychiatry*, 20 (1969), 583-91

147 Sandberg, A. A., Koepf, G. F., Ishihara, T. & Hauschka, T. S. 'An XYY Human Male', *Lancet*, ii (1961), 488-9

148 Scott, P. D. & Kahn, J. 'An XYY Patient of Above Average Intelligence as a Basis for the Review of the Psychopathology Medicolegal implications of the Syndrome, and possibilities for prevention', *Psychopathic Offenders*, ed by D. J. West (Cambridge, 1968)

149 Casey, M. D., Blank, C. E., Mobley, T., Kohn, P., Street, D. R. K., McDougall, J. M., Gooder, J. & Platts, J. *Patients with Chromosome Abnormality in Two Special Hospitals*, Special Hospitals Research Report No 2 (1971)

150 Spain, D. M., Bradess, V. A. & Eggston, A. A. 'Alcohol and Violent Death. A One Year Study of Consecutive Cases in a Representative Community', *Journal of the American Medical Association*, 146 (1951), 334-5

151 Whitlock, F. A. *Death on the Road* (1971)

152 Zylman, R. 'Accidents, Alcohol and Single Cause Explanations: Lessons from the Grand Rapids Study', *Quarterly Journal on Studies on Alcoholism (Supplement)*, 4 (1968), 212-33

153 Wolfgang, M. E. *Patterns in Criminal Homicide* (New York, 1958)

154 McGeorge, J. 'Alcohol and Crime', *Medicine, Science and the Law*, 3 (1963), 27-48

155 Shupe, L. M. 'Alcohol and Crime: A Study of the Urine Alcohol

Concentration Found in 882 Persons Arrested During or Immediately After the Commission of a Felony', *Journal of Criminal Law, Criminology, and Police Science*, 44 (1954), 661-4

156 Gibbens, T. C. N. & Silberman, M. 'Alcoholism among Prisoners', *Psychological Medicine*, 1 (1970), 73-8

157 Vogel-Sprott, M. 'Alcohol Effects on Human Behaviour under Reward and Punishment', *Psychopharmacologia*, 11 (1967), 337-44

158 Wolfgang, M. E. & Strom, R. B. 'The Relationship between Alcohol and Criminal Homicide', *Quarterly Journal of Studies in Alcohol*, 17 (1956), 411

159 Tinklenberg, J. R. & Stillman, R. C. 'Drug Use and Violence', *Violence and the Struggle for Existence*, ed by D. N. Daniels, M. F. Gilula & F. M. Ochberg (Boston, 1970)

160 Gordon, A. M. *Patterns of Delinquency in Drug Addiction*, M Phil Thesis, Univ of London (Unpublished, 1971)

161 Lewis, Sir Aubrey. 'Cannabis—A Review of the International Clinical Literature', *Cannabis - Report by the Advisory Committee on Drug Dependence* (1968)

162 Stengel, E. *Suicide and Attempted Suicide* (Harmondsworth, 1964)

163 Sainsbury, P. *Suicide in London*, Maudsley Monographs No 1 (1955)

164 Menninger, K. *Man Against Himself* (New York, 1938)

165 Blom-Cooper, L. 'Preventible Homicide', *Howard Journal*, XI (1965), 297-308

166 MacDonald, J. M. *Homicidal Threats* (Springfield, Ill, 1968)

167 Gunn, J. C. 'Forensic Psychiatry and Psychopathic Patients', *British Journal of Hospital Medicine*, 5 (1971), 260-4

8 *VIOLENT CRIME* (pp125-47)

168 McLintock, F. H. & Avison, N. H. *Crime in England and Wales* (1968)

169 McLintock, F. H. *Crimes of Violence* (1963)

170 Morris, N. & Hawkins, G. *The Honest Politician's Guide to Crime Control* (Chicago, 1969)

171 Walker, N. *Crime and Punishment in Britain*, revised ed (Edinburgh, 1968)

172 Graham, F. P. 'A Contemporary History of American Crime', *The History of Violence in America*, ed by H. D. Graham & T. R. Gurr (New York, 1969)

173 Parry, M. H. *Aggression on the Road* (1968)

174 Dept of Environment. *Road Accidents 1969* (1971)

175 MacDonald, J. M. 'Suicide and Homicide by Automobile', *American Journal of Psychiatry*, 121 (1964), 366-70

176 Gibson, E. & Klein, S. *Murder*, Home Office Studies in the Causes

of Delinquency and the Treatment of Offenders No 4 (1961)

177 Gibbens, T. C. N. 'Sane and Insane Homicide', *Journal of Criminal Law, Criminology and Police Science*, 49 (1958) 110-15

178 MacDonald, J. M. *The Murderer and his Victim* (Springfield, Ill, 1961)

179 Morris, T. & Blom-Cooper, L. *A Calendar of Murder: Criminal Homicide in England since 1957* (1964)

180 Gunn, J. C. 'Medicine and the Permissive Society', *British Journal of Hospital Medicine*, 4 (1970), 549-53

181 Caffey, J. 'Multiple Fractures in the Long Bones of Infants Suffering from Chronic Subdural Haematoma', *American Journal of Roentgenology and Radium Therapy*, 56 (1946), 163-73

182 Kempe, C. H., Silverman, F. N., Steele, B. F., Droegemueller, W. & Silver, H. K. 'The Battered Child Syndrome', *Journal of the American Medical Association*, 181 (1962), 17-24

183 Cameron, J. M., Johnson, H. R. H. & Camps, F. E. 'The Battered Child Syndrome', *Medicine, Science and the Law*, 6 (1966), 1-21

184 Skinner, A. E. & Castle, R. L. *78 Battered Children* (1969)

185 Gebhard, P. H., Gagnon, J. H., Pomeroy, W. B. & Christenson, C. V. *Sex Offenders* (1965)

186 MacDonald, J. M. *Rape, Offenders and their Victims* (Springfield, Ill, 1971)

187 McLintock, F. H. & Gibson, E. *Robbery in London* (1961)

188 Parker, T. & Allerton, R. *The Courage of his Convictions* (1962)

189 Megargee, E. I. 'Undercontrolled and Overcontrolled Personality Types in Extreme Antisocial Aggression', *Psychological Monographs 80*, No 611 (1966)

190 Blackburn, R. *Personality Types among Abnormal Homicides*, Special Hospitals Research Reports No 1 (1970)

191 Nicol, R., Gunn, J. C., Foggitt, R. & Gristwood, J. 'Quantitative Assessment of Violence in Adult and Young Offenders', *Medicine, Science and the Law*, 12 (1972), 275-82

192 Banks, C. 'Violence', *Howard Journal*, XI (1962), 13-25

9 *METHODS OF CONTROL* (pp148-75)

193 Weatherhead, A. D. & Robinson, B. M. *Firearms in Crime*, Home Office Research Studies No 4 (1970)

194 Sherif, M., Harvey, O. J., White, B. J., Hood, W. R. & Sherif, C. W. *Intergroup Conflict and Co-operation: The Robber's Cave Experiment* (Norman, Oklahoma, 1961)

195 Waskow, A. I. 'The Place of Hostility and Conflict in a Disarmed World', *Violence and War*, ed by J. H. Masserman (New York, 1963)

196 Flugel, J. C. 'Some Neglected Aspects of World Integration',

Psychological Factors of Peace and War, ed by T. H. Pear (1950)

197 Frank, J. D. *Sanity & Survival, Psychological Aspects of War and Peace* (New York, 1967)

198 Walker, N., Hammond, W. & Steer, D. 'Careers of Violence', *The Violent Offender—Reality or Illusion?*, Oxford University Penal Research Unit (Oxford, 1970)

199 Carr-Hill, R. 'Victims of our Typologies', *The Violent Offenders—Reality or Illusion?*, Oxford University Penal Research Unit (Oxford, 1970)

200 Smeed, R. J. 'Foreword', *Death on the Road*, by F. A. Whitlock (Tavistock, 1971)

201 Austin, M. *Accident Black Spot* (Harmondsworth, 1966)

Glossary

Words and expressions that have been defined in the text are not included here, but can be checked by use of the index.

AGONISTIC—combative; contest-like

ASYLUM—sanctuary; a place of refuge

AZTECS—the pre-Columbian inhabitants of Mexico during fifteenth century

BABOON—large African and South Asian monkey

CANNIBAL—a creature that eats its own species

CARNIVOROUS—flesh-eating

CASTRATION—removal of male sex organs (ie, testes)

CEREBRAL TUMOUR—a growth in the brain

CHROMOSOMES—thread-like structures found in the nucleus of living cells, which carry the genetic (qv) material

DELUSION—an idiosyncratic false belief that is not open to argument or discussion, eg, 'I am Napoleon'

DOMINANCE—the ability to rule, or command others

EEG—electroencephalogram; a recording of the brain's electrical activity

ENCEPHALITIS LETHARGICA—an infectious virus disease affecting the brain

ENDOCRINES—internal secretions or hormones

EPILEPSY—a disease characterised by episodes of lost consciousness, during which there may be a convulsion

ETHOLOGY—the study of the social life of animals by direct observation

GENETIC—inborn; inherited by cellular transmission from one generation to the next

GENUS—a class of animals or plants

GESTAPO—German Nazi secret police

GIBBON—a long-armed ape from India

HALLUCINATION—a realistic sensation which is not generated by an external stimulus, eg, a clear voice in the absence of other people

HERBIVOROUS—exclusively plant-eating

HIERARCHY—a graded and ordered social structure with ranks or positions of authority

HOMICIDE—the killing of a human being (in this book the term is not used in any specific legal sense)

HORMONES—chemicals secreted internally that act as messengers and stimulate target organs

INFANTICIDE—the murder of an infant after birth: in legal terms by its real mother before it reaches the age of 1 year

INSTINCT—an innate inherited propensity

KAMIKAZE PILOTS—Japanese pilots of World War II who deliberately dived their aeroplanes into a target (eg, an enemy ship) knowing that they would die in the process

KU KLUX KLAN—anti-negro secret society of the American Deep South

MORES—customs or conventions having the force of unwritten rules

NEURO-ANATOMY—the physical structure of the nervous system

NEURO-PHYSIOLOGY—the functioning of the nervous system

OMBUDSMAN—an official arbitrator between government and people

PANDEMIC—a wide-scale epidemic

PANSEXUAL—indiscriminate in choice of sexual partner;

both homosexual and heterosexual

PAVLOVIAN—pertaining to the ideas of the Russian psychologist Ivan Pavlov, who demonstrated that learning can take place by association

PENOLOGY—the scientific study of punishment

PHYLOGENETIC—ancestral in evolutionary terms

PREDATION—preying on other creatures

PRIMATE—highest order of mammals, include man, monkeys and apes

PSYCHIATRY—the medical specialty concerned with the treatment of mental disorder

PSYCHOANALYSIS—a form of investigation and treatment of mental and emotional disturbances by introspective methods, derived from such practitioners as Freud, Jung, Adler, and Klein

PSYCHOLOGY—the science of behaviour and mental processes

PSYCHOTIC—severe mental disease state characterised by delusions (qv) and hallucinations (qv)

PSYCHOTOMIMETICS—drugs that distort the perception of reality and produce psychotic (qv) like states

PUBERTY—the age of sexual maturity

RHESUS MONKEY—small monkey common in North India

SEX CHROMOSOMES—chromosomes (qv) that determine the sex of the individual carrying them

SUBMISSION—obedience; acceptance of authority or dominance

TEMPORAL LOBES—the parts of the brain which are situated laterally and embrace part of the limbic system as well as some areas of the neocortex associated with hearing and balance

VICTIMOLOGY—the study of the processes that lead particular individuals to become victims

VIGILANTE—one who belongs to a self-appointed group aiming to maintain a form of law and order when other forms are being defied or are nonexistent

Index